BEYOND THE
BABY
BLUES

THE COMPLETE PERINATAL ANXIETY
AND DEPRESSION HANDBOOK

By Catherine Knox, Benison O'Reilly and Seana Smith

DISCLAIMER

Beyond the Baby Blues aims to provide readers with information, but is not intended to be, and is not, a substitute for health and medical advice from a qualified health professional. Jane Curry Publishing does not guarantee or warrant the accuracy, currency, suitability or reliability of any information contained within the book. Diagnosis and treatment of a medical condition should only be undertaken by a qualified health professional and readers should always seek the advice of a qualified health professional before treatment of any condition. In reading this book you accept all risk and responsibility for losses, damages, costs or any other consequences resulting directly or indirectly from relying on information or material contained within it. To the maximum permitted by law, Jane Curry Publishing excludes all liability to any person arising directly or indirectly from using this book and any information or material in it.

First published by
Jane Curry Publishing 2011
[Wentworth Concepts Pty Ltd]
PO Box 780 Edgecliff NSW 2027 Australia
www.janecurrypublishing.com.au

National Library of Australia Cataloguing-in-publication data is available.
ISBN: 9780980812947 (pbk.)
Dewey Number: 618.76

Cover photograph: Photolibrary.com
Cover and internal design: Deborah Parry
Printed in China by 1010 Printing

CONTENTS

BEFORE WE START — AN IMPORTANT NOTE ABOUT TERMINOLOGY

It's likely that most of you are familiar with the term postnatal depression. However, with the growing recognition that depression occurs almost as commonly during pregnancy as afterwards, experts now prefer to talk about *perinatal depression. Peri* means 'around', so perinatal depression encompasses both *antenatal depression*: depression occurring during pregnancy, and *postnatal depression*: depression occurring in mothers (and occasionally fathers) in the first year after childbirth. Even this description excludes the large number of women who feel more anxious than depressed at this time. Hence *perinatal anxiety and depression* is now the term favoured by medical experts in the field and the one we have chosen to use in this book. We explain more terminology in Chapter 2.

INTRODUCTION

Children — they're a real mixed blessing aren't they?

Parenthood is that great paradox of joy and disaster. Giving birth can be an empowering and exciting experience. A new baby can bring so much joy, yet their arrival can also be an emotional roller coaster for many couples. For some women and their partners it can be an overwhelming time of stress and struggle.

There is nothing like parenthood, such swings of highs and lows, such joy and such grief, so much gained, yet so much lost.

Parenthood! It's complicated. We see very little of the realities of parenting reflected in the mainstream media that now saturates our tech-savvy society.

Wouldn't it be just fantastic if each parent-to-be, in the lead up to each pregnancy, was sent off for a weekend in the countryside? No, sorry, not just to enjoy time together, but to learn. They could be drilled and workshopped, made to think and reflect deeply on the many changes ahead: all the changes, not just newborns, nipples and nappies.

For expectant parents and for the mums and dads of newborns, babies and toddlers, the life changes are immense, and let's be honest, not all of them are good changes.

Along our journey to parenthood most of us will struggle and stumble. All too often we will feel that we are alone in this struggle, whilst around us all the other pregnant women or parents of new babies are managing well. Of course, nothing could be further from the truth.

All men and women, whether parents or potential parents, need to know that it really is ok to struggle, it's acceptable to parent imperfectly and indeed that it is typical to feel truly grim at times. All of us have times of great difficulty as we adapt to parenthood, both before and after the birth.

These struggles and the great overwhelming joy that we feel when babies enter our lives are all part of the broader emotional experience that most of us feel when we become parents.

The ups and downs of pregnancy and early parenthood swing us high and low. These are normal experiences that we don't have to think of as needing treatment — although a cup of tea and a hand with the cleaning is never to be knocked back. But when the lows come too often or dip too low, we parents deserve help, we need it.

Although in our society it is not usual to talk openly of the worst emotions that parenthood can bring, we are going to be very bold (plus honest and truthful) when we state that it is also **normal** to experience the more severe end of the parenting difficulties spectrum, to experience very real anxiety and depression.

It is estimated that almost one in five parents may experience anxiety and depression before or after childbirth. This is now a typical experience, and, crucially, in most cases very, very treatable. What **isn't** ok is for mums and dads to experience the anguish of anxiety and depression and to deal with it alone, remaining untreated.

We do not mean to sound glib or to suggest that the treatment of anxiety and depression is a simple or automatic process. We know that it is not. We know how dark are the places that anxiety and depression can take us and how each day can feel like an endless battle to survive. We know how bone-achingly awful sleep deprivation can be, and how menacing is its twin, insomnia. But we also do know that in the vast majority of cases the physical and mental symptoms can be treated and can in most cases be alleviated over time.

This book aims to provide a comprehensive guide to mood disorders, with an emphasis on anxiety and depression, before and after childbirth. You will find in these pages all the serious and scientific things you need to know, whether you are in the midst of this yourself, helping someone who is, or treating sufferers as a professional or allied health provider.

You will also find here all the best places to locate resources and more information; the medical benefits, websites, books and blogs you need to assist you.

This book is also steeped in personal experience and the reflections of many generous people. We will tell you of our own experiences and we will share with you many stories from brave and generous contributors.

We hope to illustrate that those who are currently experiencing perinatal anxiety and depression will recover and may indeed be stronger for it. Parents who have recovered often say that their experiences have improved their lives.

Hopefully, like us, you may go on to be 'good enough' mothers and fathers, who are good enough to yourselves too.

There are three co-authors of this book, plus one hard-working publisher. Between us we have 15 children, 13 boys and two girls, who are currently aged 3 to 19 years. Quite a handful!

Three of us have experienced severe anxiety and depression before or after childbirth. We are all now recovered, but changed by our experiences, just as we have been by parenthood. We are all more aware of our own emotional health; we know when we are starting to sink into low moods. We are more able to seek help so that we are not so seriously affected as we were when our children were little.

We are all very passionate about supporting new parents, as are the many families, professionals, academics and researchers who have been so generous with their help and support.

The realities of pregnancy and parenting can bring great stress and often induce both anxiety and depression in parents and parents-to-be. But we hope to emphasise in this book that, whilst none of us would choose to experience this, it's ok; it's understandable, it's treatable.

Start talking about perinatal anxiety and depression — we did and we're still chatting as we send this book off to press.

1
THE TRANSITION TO PARENTHOOD

I was as well prepared as I could have been. I did plenty of reading, went to parenting classes and quizzed lots of other mums. But no amount of preparation can fully prepare you for the experience.

I was surprised by the loneliness of being a first time parent and remember spending a lot of time just wandering around the mall to while away the time during the day.

I think I knew the brutal reality of having kids; that it's joyous one moment and horrendous the next; and that's been my experience.

Carefully managed images of celebrity mothers, 'post baby' bodies on display, accessorised by doting partners and serenely sleeping offspring — this message of parenthood is common in women's magazines, but it is rewriting reality. It has a name — Perfect Parent

Syndrome — and the yummy mummies sipping their lattes, off to the gym, pushing their designer strollers are aspiring to live this fantasy. The more realistic images of stunned parents, struggling because of lack of sleep but just managing to get by, cannot be found in our mainstream media, not even in the parenting magazines where even the babies can look airbrushed.

Parenting is an amazing journey but one that brings many challenges. It is full of wonderful rewards and intense love but it needs to be grounded in reality.

Of course, it isn't the case that there are no balanced descriptions of the typical ups and downs of parenthood. However, they are less obvious and we often don't find them until we are months or years down the track. Through the 'mummy bloggers' (there are dozens in Australia and thousands throughout the world) and the online social networks, our real lives are reflected. But you don't see these parents on the shelves at the supermarket.

> *It was more of a shock than I expected, it was like being in a car crash, and my life has never been the same since. I didn't expect to have such great highs and such terrible lows.*

> **I thought I was ready but once the twins were born I realised I had no idea what was in store.**

> *The happy times were great: that first day in hospital; just my little boy and me; lots of cuddles. I still have lots of them too, although parenting is a real challenge sometimes.*

Having a baby changes everything. The adjustment to parenthood is possibly the most significant physical, emotional and social change we will ever have to deal with in our lives. While the arrival of a baby can be an exciting time for many parents, the changes that the new baby brings can also create feelings of grief and loss. Most importantly our relationships with those around us change as we adapt to our new identities of mother and father. It is not uncommon to mourn the loss of our independence, our freedom, even our pre-baby identity.

For many of us, the realisation of the enormity of our new situation can come as a shock — it has been described by one GP as 'a stunned bunny in the headlights' shock. While some parents may make the adjustment reasonably easily, most will struggle with different aspects of parenthood, finding the transition to be far more complex than they ever imagined.

What can make this time even more challenging is the belief that it should come naturally — after all it's only biology. It's very easy to feel confused and even disappointed if the reality does not match up to the happy family messages you have been receiving.

How can something so ordinary feel so extraordinary when it happens to you? Parents are ubiquitous. At any given moment around the world there are babies being born. Yet, when you become the mother or father you can feel like you are the only person experiencing this remarkable life event.

Becoming a parent is such a tumultuous experience. It can bring great joy and a new experience of love. It can be overwhelmingly exciting. It can also just be overwhelming.

I don't think you can really prepare for parenthood. I think you can't. It's like my experience of emigrating to a foreign country. You might have visited the place on holiday but the reality of living there is totally different. Starting a family is the same.

Few of us seem prepared for this reality, particularly in our linear and often fragmented Western society where we can often be more connected to our peer group than to our extended family. New parents may have had little experience around babies before their own comes along.

I was totally ignorant of what life with a baby would be like. I had no close friends with small children, and I had very little experience. I knew they would be consuming, but I was not prepared for the constant sleep deprivation, the mental fatigue and the feeling of being alone. Logically I knew what would happen, but reality was different.

My youngest sister seemed to find the changes so much easier than I did, maybe because some of her friends had had babies when they were very young, and she had been around babysitting and just seeing what life with a baby was really like. I had been a real career girl and none of my friends had babies young.

CONGRATULATIONS — HERE IS YOUR BABY

Many of us begin our parenthood journey with a forced reality check: a birth that was difficult and painful, sitting alone in a hospital bed after the drama, holding a new baby and wondering how we got there, overwhelmed by the realisation that we are now responsible for this brand new human and questioning what to do next.

I hadn't understood how much giving birth would hurt. How much noise a baby can make at night. How a baby crying emotionally upsets you. That it can take up to two months to learn to breastfeed.

Birth was a huge shock to me — I thought I was going to die.

The heightened surveillance of pregnancy is often replaced by the isolation of life with a new baby. Pregnant women, particularly in our society, can be portrayed in the media as sexy, sassy, fun and funky. Society gives them status. The reality of the birth can change all this. Life as a new mother can in contrast be messy, exhausting, boring and lonely.

Most of my low points would be associated with lack of sleep or the relentlessness of two small babies.

I fell madly in love with my little boy but had the usual feelings of incompetence settling him, breastfeeding (initially at least) etc. I went back to work fairly quickly, which was the right thing for me.

If our pre-birth fantasies ever included a baby, it was always perfect, but no baby is perfect. Very few couples are prepared for the possibility of having a baby that will require extra help and attention. A baby that cries constantly and sleeps rarely can challenge even the most patient parent. And sometimes the birth can bring to the surface feelings of grief over earlier pregnancy losses, miscarriages or terminations, for both partners.

Just when any mother is wondering where to go for help, there is an entire industry waiting out there to direct her: an industry easily accessible via the internet, the bookshop, or the specialist service providers. We are surrounded by messages telling us how a good mother should behave; the problem is that these messages are often contradictory and confusing.

Given these conditions, it's a wonder that any Australian mothers manage to get on with their lives, regroup and rebuild after the birth.

Caring for a little baby can be the most remarkable experience for a new mother or father. Parents with older children often harbour nostalgic memories of that unique time in their lives. However, the demands can also be relentless and few new parents are prepared for the tiring repetitive nature of the work. Above all, parenting requires resilience.

Motherhood can be magical. It can also be mundane.

DIFFERENT SOCIETIES, DIFFERENT GENERATIONS AND DIFFERENT ATTITUDES TO MOTHERS

Parenthood, and motherhood in particular, should be the great connector. Mothers across the world, irrespective of age, race or religion, have the shared experience of giving birth, of feeling the responsibility for a brand new life. Mothers across the generations should also be connected through their experiences.

The journey that is parenting should be shared. Yet, all too commonly in our society, each mother appears to set off on this journey as if she is the first explorer, forging her singular way ahead into unknown lands.

Historically in Western societies new mothers were cared for by their mothers and/or their community. New mothers were mothered, the physical demands of giving birth and looking after a newborn acknowledged by this care. Even today, in many communities around the world, new mothers are nurtured. A time period may be set aside after the birth for the mother to recover. In the United Kingdom, ten days was considered the appropriate time for a mother to 'lie in'. This has now become the standard period that many new mothers in Britain will receive midwife visits. In Mexico, a typical time frame for nurturing the new mother is 30–40 days. Often rituals surrounding birth, the newborn and the new mother are carried out during this time; whilst at first glance these may seem primitive and rooted in superstition, they do at least acknowledge that a significant rite of passage has taken place.

Even during the 1950s and 1960s in Australia, mothers were expected to take a number of weeks to recover after giving birth. This compares starkly with the attitude today, where mothers will only spend three or four days in hospital before heading home to care for this new baby, often with very limited support. While this may reflect the hospital bottom line rather than any particular attitude to mothers, it sends a strong message that we should just 'get up and get on with it'.

Rituals tend to be reaffirming. However, an Indian friend of mine was not so sure at one stage. Her mother had flown from Delhi to care for her after her first baby was born, acting as gate keeper and setting strict conditions on diet and behaviour. One particular point of conflict was over her hair, which she was forbidden to wash. Greasy hair notwithstanding, at least my friend was nurtured and her special status as a new mother was acknowledged in a way that connected her with her community!

Apart from the occasional baby shower, flowers and celebratory drinks, our society has very few birth rituals. It's a lost opportunity to value mothers and fathers; to acknowledge their hard work and allow them some time to adjust emotionally and physically to their new role. In a practical sense, the federal government baby bonus and paid parental leave scheme are steps in the right direction, but Australia still lags behind many Western countries in the support it provides to new parents.

Many contemporary Australian families are being created without strong social networks. Young couples may live in different locations to their family or friends. They may have no obvious community to turn to and can feel isolated. While there are different ways parents can connect to their new community this can take time and effort.

PARENTING — HOW DO WE LEARN THESE SKILLS?

Our personal experiences of childhood and adolescence and our own families will have a significant impact on the way we parent. Pregnancy is a perfect time to reflect on this. Before the baby is born it is really worthwhile to spend some time as a couple talking about the interactions that occurred in your families as you were growing up.

Whether we like it or not our parents are our main role models. Indeed, the way we relate to the outside world is greatly influenced by our family dynamics and what we learnt from our parents. This is a great opportunity to consider the way that you were parented. Most of us will be able to point out the good, the bad and the ugly in our parents' behaviours. Some patterns of behaviour we might like to copy, others we might swear never to copy ... until that day we catch ourselves doing or saying something and suddenly think 'Oh no I'm turning into my mother!'

Finding time to talk to your partner before you start your own family is very helpful. You might discover all sorts of practical differences between your childhood experiences — how different families manage conflict and stress as well as how positive emotions are expressed. Some families are very demonstrative, while others can be very reserved and self-contained. Some personality styles like to confront situations head on while others will avoid them at all cost, others fall somewhere in between.

Things that you could include in your discussions:
- our own parents (the positives and negatives) and what we can learn from that
- our perspectives on how we will be as a parent
- our expectations of parenting
- our expectations of our relationships and ourselves as individuals
- the positive things we are looking forward to
- what some of the challenges might be
- how we intend to deal with the challenges

Expectations of parenthood and adjusting to reality

The transition to parenthood probably has as many variations and as many ups and downs as there are parents! Our contributors really got their teeth stuck into telling us about their experiences. Here are just some of them:

There is nothing that can prepare you for the changes, I think it is the acceptance that it is OK for life to change and that it is not a bad thing. It is a different life, better in a way and worse in a way.

My expectations were that life would pretty much remain as normal, baby would wake, smile lots and sleep on cue. Basically be the 'perfect child'. I had managed teams of people and a large customer base, had a big budget — this would be a breeze compared to that.

I think it would be abnormal not to feel awful at times, all that sleep deprivation and another person you are wholly responsible for, the life changing enormity of it all.

I was surprised by how life was after the baby was born. I have always wanted children and knew it would be difficult at times, especially the sleep deprivation; however, I wasn't prepared for the reality. The ups and downs and the constant nature of having a baby really took its toll on me.

I was excited about my pregnancy and even when I had my first I was so happy to be a mum finally. The low moments only started when I had more than one child to cope with.

The hardest transition was with my first who was a big baby and constantly hungry. I breastfed her for 21 months but the initial six–eight weeks were hard work.

The myths of motherhood tell us what it should be like to be pregnant and have a baby. It is all happy faces and happy stories where the new mum instantly adores her baby. My advice to anyone is that these are only myths.

Common adjustments parents may need to negotiate

Loss of control and freedom

Many of us women have spent years controlling our own destinies. You may have been used to making all the decisions about your own life. Thus the period around pregnancy may be the first time you are subjected to judgemental comments and unsolicited advice. Pregnancy may be your first experience of feeling the control you have previously had slowly slipping away. For some couples loss of control begins even earlier, when a pregnancy is difficult to achieve; for others this loss of control occurs when the pregnancy is unplanned.

The chances are that, as an Australian woman, you will only give birth a few times, so there may be a lot of emotional energy invested in making sure these experiences measure up to some personal fantasy. Most of us have certain expectations for the birth, ranging from demanding an elective caesarean at a particular time and date, to planning a spiritual homebirth, and every variation in between. When expectations are not realised — and that's very common — many women feel they have lost control of the situation and this can be distressing.

And after that little baby is born most couples experience a period of anarchy as their lives revolve around responding to the ever-changing and extraordinary needs of this small person. Leaving the house is never quite the same again; it is no longer as simple as walking out the door on a spontaneous whim. A quick catch up with friends is no longer quick. Every activity requires precision planning. To begin with there's the timing of a sleeping or wakeful baby, then there's the pram, the wraps, the bag with the changes of clothes, the nappies, perhaps bottles ...

Your personal pregnancy and parenthood journey can illicit public comment

Having lived life as a private person many women are quite shocked to find that once they become pregnant and then have a baby they appear to become public property. All mothers have stories of 'advice' they've received from friends, family, and even random strangers. Of course helpful advice and suggestions from caring friends and family are wonderful. Judgemental comments from random strangers are not. For many women these unhelpful comments may even cause feelings of confusion and real guilt, perhaps for the first time.

Secret mothers' business has morphed into the cult of perfection. Perhaps a new theory of parenting is required — the chaos theory — grounded in the principle of 'the good enough mother'.

I never went into motherhood expecting to be the perfect mother and I think that saved me from unrealistic expectations. I also knew I should go back to work; I'm no 'earth mother'.

Perfect parenthood is not the aim. We all just need to feel comfortable with the choices and decisions we make as parents.

Changes in identity and roles

No matter how positively you might view your new role as a parent, it will still cause a significant change in where you sit in society and how you are viewed by the world. This can take some getting used to. For some women this can include a perceived loss of social status, particularly if their identity was wrapped up in their work and career.

Many new fathers find this adjustment equally difficult. While mothers are dealing with their loss of self, many new fathers report feeling the loss of their partners, they feel physically and emotionally replaced by this small creature. No longer the single focus in their partner's lives, fathers can even experience jealousy and some may try to escape the domestic chaos through their work.

While many couples may have negotiated the domestic sphere relatively equally before parenthood, this area can become contentious after the arrival of the new baby. In most cases, it is mothers who spend at least the first few months at home looking after their baby and running the house. This change can sometimes lead to resentment, particularly if women feel that the work that they are doing is unrecognised.

Changes in responsibilities

All new parents take a bit of time to adjust to their new responsibilities. There is often an overwhelming feeling of responsibility in caring for the physical and emotional needs of a new baby. Added to this is the responsibility of financially supporting a growing family, which causes stress for both parents. The baby's arrival may have precipitated a home renovation or move, and in many cases the loss of one partner's financial contribution, at least for a while, has a huge impact.

While some mothers will have days when they just want to give their baby back, fathers will often wish that they could have their partner back. Some may perhaps vocalise their frustration and stress by wondering out loud about when their partner will get a real job and start earning some money again. Heightened emotions may cause a major disconnect between former happily functional couples.

Sleep deprivation

Exhaustion is probably the most common issue for new parents. We all know that feeling tired and emotional can colour our perception of the world — it's hard to be enthusiastic about life on just two hours' sleep. It can sometimes be hard to feel love for a baby who has led you to this state. As parents, the best we can do is to try and anticipate the weariness of the first few months and attempt to manage as best we can.

Many new parents harbour subversive thoughts in the small hours of the morning, particularly after spending hours trying to settle their baby. But then, when that same baby is lying asleep, those same parents can watch in wonder and experience an overwhelming protective love for this beautiful being they have created.

Getting to know your baby and finding a sense of purpose

Many women find the formless days of early motherhood difficult, particularly if they have left the structure of the workforce. They may finish the day feeling exhausted, yet wondering what they have actually achieved, knowing that after a few hours sleep they will have to get up and start all over again.

Some women find it takes a while to get to know their baby. It's not always 'love at first sight'. If this is your situation we hope you feel comforted by the fact that you are not alone in feeling this way. Sometimes the love simply develops as you get to know your baby. This can take months, even years, in some cases.

Feeling a loss of social relevance can be a real problem for some mothers. It's essential for us all to remember that being a parent is actually the most worthwhile and important job that we will ever do.

It was amazing seeing the twins born. Then the first double breastfeed, watching them sleeping and looking so carefree. I felt a connection with my son when he was a few days old where I felt like we'd met before. I loved watching all his firsts; lifting his head, crawling, grabbing for a spoon, talking, walking, the lot. With the twins it's been different. I am still enjoying their firsts now although they are very different; first time off on bus alone, first cycle to friends alone. Any spontaneous gestures of goodwill, kindness or love, their aliveness and wonder at the world, their questioning minds, their sense of fairness and justice still untainted, and I love being snuggled up reading a book or watching a movie, the cuddles and hugs, and so on and so on....

Finding time to spend with each other and by yourself

It's not so easy to spend time together when a new baby enters your relationship. Often new parents need to be proactive in creating some couple time, even if it's just for a coffee and a chat. Any opportunity to communicate your feelings to each other during these early weeks should always be taken.

You as an individual also need time. While personal time may be elusive to begin with, try not to forget that even though you have become a parent, you are also still you.

Breastfeeding

Breastfeeding may well be natural but it certainly does not come naturally to all mothers. Some mothers may not be able to breastfeed for a host of reasons. Breastfeeding can provide essential nutrients and beautiful bonding experiences, but it may also provide some mothers with a total loss of self esteem. The stresses that many couples go through during this period should not be underestimated. It is a highly emotive area, involving different groups and individuals with their conflicting agendas, but ultimately it is the mother who needs to make the final decision on how her baby will be fed. It's worthwhile remembering that no one can tell in a class of five year olds who was breastfed and who was bottle fed.

I didn't realise how long it would take to breastfeed — I felt like a failure as I needed so many pillows and felt like I'd never get to leave the house again.

I spent my childbearing years in a state of perpetual jealousy of my friends who enjoyed breastfeeding with ease. There they would sit, relaxed, chatting over a cup of tea, baby happily slurping away at the breast.

My experiences, and they were numerous and determined, involved outright nipple rejection, yelling (the baby), crying (me), cracked nipples, bleeding nipples, tears, oozing puss, mastitis, hand expressing colostrum, tears, breast pumps, and finally the indignity of being questioned about 'my choice' to bottle feed, more tears. I left a trail of 'failed' lactation consultants in my wake.

Be prepared for a period of adjustment

Most new parents struggle for a while or from time to time, others jump into their new role full of enthusiasm and anticipating enjoyment, and for some mothers, the 'new mummy' thing just doesn't happen at all. The experiences of new parents are wide ranging and we should try not to get too hung up about what experiences can be considered 'normal'. 'Normal' is such a subjective term and the evidence suggests that some level of what we might view as dysfunction is in fact 'normal'.

When reality appears in the guise of sleepless nights, cracked nipples, crying babies and foggy minds, we may look deep into ourselves and wonder if we have the capacity to manage the job of parenthood. In our competitive and sometimes judgemental world, many mothers who feel this way may be reluctant to expose their innermost thoughts to others.

Statistics suggest that up to 16% of new mothers suffer from postnatal anxiety and depression. Ten percent of pregnant women experience antenatal anxiety and depression. Up to 10% of fathers also suffer from postnatal anxiety and depression.

Outside the vast range of 'normal' is where those statistics are located, brought to life by the real people who are suffering from perinatal mood disorders. Their world has been turned upside down by the arrival of their baby and this book is dedicated to them.

Thoughts on a most difficult transition — Cathie Knox's story

I stared down at the blotchy, scrunched up face, red forceps marks carving deep lines through the fat cheeks. The baby, this alien creature, his face peering out from the tightly wrapped cloth had been unceremoniously thrust into my arms. What had just happened to me? I was in severe physical and emotional shock. My husband was in such an emotional state he had left the room. This was it. Welcome to parenthood.

For nine months I fantasised about the herbal birth — the ultimate spiritual experience. Somehow real life got in the way, pushing aside the whale music and the birthing pool. In fact, reality was so far from my expectations that I was left traumatised. Reality was loud, bustling and chaotic. And that was how it was to remain for many years to come.

My fantasies stopped at the birth. I had not considered my life as a mother. I had no preconceived ideas of what lay before me. I think this is a common experience for many women giving birth in Australia today. I had no experience of babies, and no notion of how life would unfold as a mother with a new baby.

We arrived at the hospital as a couple, but left as a family. Driving home so carefully with the baby snug in his capsule I was overcome with the realisation that my world had just undergone a seismic shift but no-one else seemed to have noticed.

Looking back at my own personal journey into motherhood confirms how significantly delusional I was. I had to prove to the world that I could cope. My 'type A' personality just wouldn't let go as I attempted to maintain tidiness and order and total control over every aspect of my life. It makes me feel very sad that we were not able to just 'be'. There was so little time to consider our new place in the world and to simply enjoy our baby.

Like many mothers over the last 20 years or so I took maternity leave. I fully anticipated returning to my career a few months after the baby was born. That was in fact what I ended up doing, but the intervening months were not at all what I had expected.

I lived in a twilight zone of exhaustion, ruled by the demands of an alien creature. I felt like I had entered some 1950s time warp as I struggled to come to terms with my busy and tiring days being unrecognised and undervalued by the world I had left behind.

My shapeless days were spent feeding, cleaning and nurturing my baby while at the same time desperately failing to maintain domestic order. For 32 years I had been defined by who I was. It was becoming increasingly apparent to me that I was now being defined by my relationships: wife and mother. I had moved from being an independent woman with my own desires and my independent interaction with the world to being a mother whose every interaction with the outside world was mediated through my baby.

I was lucky to have a caring family and good friends around. I did enjoy seeing them often but I couldn't share my private thoughts with them.

My husband, like many other new fathers around him, could not understand these conflicting feelings: partly as I was unable to articulate them clearly at the time, and partly because he was just as confused. Although enthusiastically anticipating fatherhood he began to feel increasingly alienated by the whole process.

I loved my baby desperately; I just wasn't so sure that I loved being a mother — that took a lot of time, care and attention, and some significant adjustments. Even though mine was a rather delayed love of motherhood it was no less wonderful. The roller coaster ride is still continuing — what an amazing adventure!

We asked our contributors if there were things they knew now that they wished they had known before their children were born and there were many responses! Here are some of them:

Things I wish I had known:
- That life is never the same again in good and bad ways.
- How to relax and not stress about the little things.
- That you don't change when you become a mother. You are still 'you', but you have a child to look after.
- That how you give birth (natural or with intervention) and whether you can breastfeed are ultimately unimportant as long as your baby is ok. Parenting is a long haul.
- That breastfeeding can be difficult and painful.
- That it is important to relax and have lower expectations of myself, to compare myself less to others. That no one was actually judging me although it felt like everyone was.
- That motherhood is no fairytale. However, had I known this I may never have had children and I now wouldn't swap them for the world.

2
WHY DO I FEEL SO AWFUL?

After the birth, I immediately felt isolated, even in hospital. I felt 'on display' to visitors. I had no family of my own to visit me. I felt exposed, realising my husband was completely unable to show love and empathy. I was in prison. I felt lonely, empty, black, desperate… I felt I was a failure. I covered so much up. No-one knew I felt so dark.

There were times when the anxiety grew, especially when the baby wouldn't settle. It was very difficult not to think it was something I was doing wrong, that I was a bad mother. This was really hard, especially since I had always dreamed of being a mother and really thought it would be fantastic all the time.

It felt like a big black hole. It felt like I was being constantly attacked. I felt a failure, as everyone else seemed to be coping. Also being told by your parents that you 'just need to get on with it' didn't help.

'Baby joy!' cries out the magazine at the supermarket counter. Inside its pages will be a happy celebrity couple displaying their growing baby bump or a photo shoot of the new mum and dad smiling over a serene and sleeping infant. However, these images are more grounded in fantasy than reality. Babies may bring joy but they also bring huge challenges: loss of income, loss of independence, constant tiredness and worries about feeding, settling, and safety. American author and depression survivor, Shoshanna Bennett, exposes a pervading myth when she says, 'Being a new mother is *not* supposed to be the happiest time of your life.'[1]

For a significant proportion of new mothers there will be little baby joy at all, as the stories above clearly show. It's possible the words of *these* new mums reflect some of your own feelings — or the feelings of someone close to you — right now. If so, you may be comforted to know you are not alone. Studies have found that around one in ten women will experience significant depression during pregnancy, with this rate rising to 16% — about one in six women — in the first year after the birth.[2] Many of these women will also develop crippling anxiety, and others the more serious but rarer conditions of *bipolar disorder* or *puerperal psychosis* (discussed in more detail on page 39).

Later chapters will talk about the steps involved in getting help and treatment for perinatal anxiety and depression, hopefully giving you a path to follow so that you can recover some of that baby joy that seems so elusive right now. However, first we have to have a clear idea of the issues we are facing. This chapter and Chapter 3 will explain in detail what we mean by the terms *depression* and *anxiety*, and will discuss their possible causes and how symptoms may manifest themselves in your life.

WHAT IS DEPRESSION?

It's estimated that around one million Australian adults live with depression each year. Depression is therefore a common illness, yet it remains poorly understood.

All of us have felt 'sad', 'down' or even 'depressed' at some point in our life, maybe after a relationship breakup or the loss of a loved one, but eventually we recover from these setbacks. Unfortunately for some people — for a variety of reasons, which may be genetic, psychological or circumstantial (see Chapter 3) — depression can cease being an emotion and become an illness. Depression of this type may be called *clinical depression* or a *depressive disorder*.

Depression is also sometimes referred to as a *mood disorder*, because low mood is the main underlying feature. (Another well known mood disorder is *bipolar disorder*). Depression may either be classified as *major depression* or *minor depression*, depending on the severity of the symptoms.

Unlike other familiar illnesses such as asthma or heart disease, depression has no obvious physical signs, and the vague, non-specific symptoms that accompany it, such as fatigue, insomnia and weight changes, can be easy to dismiss as being 'all in the mind'. However, clinical depression is a serious illness that requires treatment — it's not something you can just 'snap out of', despite what some people might say.

Medical researchers are now using brain-imaging technologies, such as magnetic resonance imaging (MRI) and positron emission tomography (PET), to study people with depression. By comparing the brains of these individuals with those of non-depressed people, researchers have been able to identify changes to regions of the brain thought to be involved in the control of mood. In addition, scientists have found that the function of three important *neurotransmitters* (chemical messengers) — serotonin, noradrenaline and dopamine — is disrupted in clinical depression. Clinical depression is now understood to be a real, biological illness; however, why these changes happen is still not properly understood.

Symptoms of depression

According to the *Diagnostic and Statistical Manual of Mental Disorders, 4th edition — Text Revision* (DSM-IV-TR),[3] one of the key diagnostic manuals used by health professionals, you may be suffering from depression if you have experienced **at least two weeks** of:

a low or depressed mood most of every day, and/or

a loss of interest or pleasure in almost all activities most of every day

These mood changes will generally be accompanied by some (but not necessarily all) of the following signs:

- changes in appetite or weight
- insomnia or over-sleepiness
- fatigue ('no energy')
- agitation or restlessness
- feelings of worthlessness or guilt
- indecisiveness/an inability to concentrate
- recurrent thoughts of death or suicide.

We will talk much more about the signs of depression, below, but if you feel this list describes how you are currently feeling **and** these symptoms are severe enough to interfere with your ability to function in daily life, we recommend you speak to your doctor as soon as possible about getting an assessment.

WHAT IS ANXIETY?

Like depression, anxiety is an expected human reaction to certain of life stresses: job pressures, public speaking, exams, ill health, even the first date with a new romantic partner. However, for some people anxiety may develop for no apparent reason, and/or intrude so much into their lives that it becomes a debilitating illness. In this situation a person may be diagnosed with an *anxiety disorder*.

Anxiety disorders can present in many different ways:

Generalised anxiety disorder (GAD) People with GAD worry chronically and excessively about everyday things, such as finances and relationships. Symptoms such as irritability, concentration problems, restlessness, insomnia, and muscle tension result.

Phobia A phobia is an excessive and unreasonable fear of a specific object or situation. Sufferers will often go to great lengths to avoid their phobia. Common phobias include: *social phobia*, a fear of social situations and *agoraphobia*, a fear of open spaces. These phobias can become so serious that they severely impact on a person's capacity to function in everyday life; for example, they may develop a fear of leaving the house unaccompanied.

Obsessive compulsive disorder (OCD) People with OCD have intrusive, repetitive thoughts and fears, which they know are irrational but cannot control. These are referred to as *obsessions*. Examples include: fear of forgetting to turn off appliances or fear of germs from 'unclean' objects, such as door handles and toilets. OCD sufferers will commonly perform certain rituals or *compulsions* (eg hand washing, checking appliances, repeating words silently) in an effort to reduce their anxiety, although these will only provide temporary relief. Obsessions and compulsions are associated with severe anxiety and with time can become so intrusive that they interfere with all aspects of daily life.

Posttraumatic stress disorder (PTSD) PTSD can develop after a person experiences or witnesses a severely distressing or disturbing event, such as a war, major accident, or physical or sexual abuse. Symptoms of PTSD include: flashbacks and nightmares, emotional detachment, startling easily, heightened awareness and irritability.

Panic disorder A *panic attack* is an intense feeling of fear and anxiety that can strike suddenly with no warning. Symptoms may include feelings of dread, shortness of breath, sweating, lightheadedness and chest pain. For many people panic attacks happen only occasionally, but for others a vicious cycle can develop and they will worry constantly about future episodes. Frequent, repeated panic attacks can lead to a diagnosis of panic disorder. If prolonged and untreated, panic disorder can become associated with agoraphobia, as people get so fearful about having a panic attack they become too scared to leave the house.

Anxiety disorders frequently go hand in hand with depression; for example someone may have a primary diagnosis of depression but also have panic attacks or symptoms of OCD. This is also true in the postnatal period and it is important to detect and treat both conditions.[4]

Women are particularly vulnerable to anxiety and depression

Depression and anxiety disorders are more common in women than men. A recent *prevalence* study found that one in three Australian women had experienced depression or an anxiety disorder at some stage in their life.[5] Given this finding, it's hardly surprising to discover that anxiety and depression can occur perinatally; in fact women appear to be particularly vulnerable to mental health disorders at this time.

ANXIETY AND DEPRESSION DURING PREGNANCY

Unfortunately the 'glow of pregnancy' is no guarantee against anxiety and depression. Many women feel more 'emotional' whilst pregnant. Tearfulness and mood swings are common, and it's thought that changing levels of oestrogen and progesterone may contribute to this. For some women, these mood changes will become so severe and prolonged that they will start affecting their ability to function in daily life. These women may go on to be diagnosed with *antenatal depression*.

We say 'may go on to be diagnosed' because unfortunately antenatal depression is often missed by health professionals. Many cases of apparent postnatal depression — it was estimated up to 40% in one study — are actually cases of antenatal depression that have gone unrecognised and untreated.[2]

Antenatal depression can develop as a reaction to the pregnancy itself. About half of all pregnancies are unplanned, and presumably some of these are unwanted, or at least badly timed. Women may feel unprepared for their new role as a mother and anxious about the birth. Pregnancy also brings physical changes and not all these are welcome — morning sickness, weight gain, back pain, heartburn and sleeplessness can all affect mood. Other life stresses can also play a part. Life does not immediately become uncomplicated because a baby is on the way — money may be tight, partners may lose jobs or walk out, or elderly parents may pass away, leaving the new mother without support.

Women who have had previous problems with anxiety, or complications during an earlier pregnancy, such as miscarriage or stillbirth, are particularly prone to anxiety at this time. Women who report significant anxiety symptoms during pregnancy are at higher risk of postnatal depression.

Mothers who experienced trauma in childhood (eg abuse or the loss of a parent) may find it particularly difficult to make the transition to parenthood; they often lack a role model for what it means to be a parent. For women who have children later in life, it may be difficult to abandon their strongly developed sense of identity as a productive member of the workforce in order to become a mother.

Sometimes women will be already receiving treatment for anxiety and depression when their pregnancy is confirmed. In this situation it's very common for women to stop taking their medication because of concerns for the baby's welfare. Unfortunately this, more often than not, leads to relapse. So, if you become pregnant whilst taking an antidepressant it is very important you don't go 'cold turkey', especially without telling your doctor. The research is increasingly reassuring about the safety of the newer antidepressants in pregnancy, with respect to the potential for increasing birth defects (see Chapter 7). For some women, staying on an effective, low dose of antidepressant under close medical supervision may be a better long term option — for both mother **and** baby — than battling on without support.

Anxiety and depression during pregnancy — what does it look like?

Depression can be easy to miss during pregnancy because some of the symptoms, such as poor sleep, fatigue and decreased libido are also the signs of pregnancy. Similarly, mood swings and worry can easily be dismissed as 'hormonal'.

How do we distinguish between the normal ups and downs of pregnancy and a genuine case of anxiety and depression? This is not an exhaustive list, but a pregnant woman with depression and/ or anxiety may:

- eat poorly, sometimes losing rather than gaining weight
- never feel rested, even after taking a nap
- lose the ability to experience pleasure and feel sad or 'numb'
- have trouble concentrating and making decisions*
- have low self-esteem
- neglect her appearance
- feel guilty for not looking forward to the baby
- feel anxious about how she will cope with the delivery and caring for the baby
- have panic attacks
- feel a loss of control about weight gain, physical changes, the birth (as the professionals 'take charge'), even her sense of individuality
- worry constantly about the health of the unborn baby, despite reassurance from midwives and doctors
- have trouble sleeping, because of racing, anxious thoughts, rather than the physical discomforts of pregnancy (eg needing to go to bathroom).

I think I was depressed even before the baby came, I couldn't sleep very well and would sometimes go out and drive the car around at 2am and 3am, my mind seething with thoughts, trying desperately to work out how I could escape from my life which I felt was suffocating me. Yes, sounds like depression, although I didn't think of it that way at the time.

Looking back to when I was pregnant, I felt anxious and worried — I think I was depressed — I felt very unsure about what was to come. My dad had died and I had got back from my trip from the UK, having buried him and left my mum there. I got pregnant straightaway and did not get to deal with these events.

I felt like I had lost control of my life and my own body, as if it had been invaded by an alien, and it was all my husband's fault.

Depression during pregnancy is of particular concern because it may cause the woman to:
- not get proper antenatal care
- self-medicate with alcohol, street drugs and cigarettes, all of which may be harmful to the baby.

I told no-one I was pregnant, hoping it would just go away. I refused to have any antenatal care until I was about 25 weeks. I was dealing with serious denial. No-one would talk to me about my feelings — friends or professionals.

If this sounds like you, or someone close to you, it's really important that you speak to your doctor or midwife as soon as possible; unless you are having suicidal thoughts, when you should talk to someone **immediately**.

Recent research indicates that untreated antenatal anxiety and depression may not be good for the baby, with some studies suggesting a link between severe symptoms and premature birth, low birth-weight babies, and longer-term emotional and behavioural problems in the child. Also, as antenatal anxiety and depression is the most important risk factor for postnatal depression, you may be setting yourself up for further problems after your baby is born.

*A recent Australian study found that pregnancy and childbirth per se do not negatively affect memory and concentration. The authors suggested that the so called 'baby brain' might actually be a sign of anxiety and depression in some women.

AFTER THE BABY ARRIVES — POSTNATAL ANXIETY AND DEPRESSION

Initially I was ok but things changed when my baby was about three weeks old. He was awake more often, cried more and needed a lot of help settling. My husband was back at work and my parents weren't there every day. I was left alone with the baby and was trying to get into a routine. I think the initial excitement had died down and it was time to get on with life. This is when it really hit me and I started to feel really depressed.

Maternal exhaustion, depressed mood, heightened emotions, heightened anxiety and preoccupation with infant issues like feeding are normal reactions to the significant event of giving birth. But in cases where perinatal mood disorder is developing these symptoms start intruding on the person's daily level of functioning: cognitively, physically, emotionally, socially, spiritually etc. And even with increased sleep and support these symptoms do not go away. (health professional)

Childbirth and new motherhood is a time of huge upheaval. Even women who deliver a healthy baby after a textbook delivery can experience an emotional letdown afterwards, as the 24-hour reality of caring for a newborn sinks in. For other women the birth experience will be less than ideal. They may feel overwhelmed, out of their depth, and disappointed that the euphoria they were expecting never came.

Many, in fact, most women, will go on to experience the 'baby blues' at this time.

> The **'baby blues'** refer to a brief period of mood swings, tearfulness and anxiety that is very common amongst new mums in the first week after giving birth. Symptoms tend to appear 3–5 days after giving birth and generally resolve in a week or two. The baby blues shouldn't affect your ability to care for your baby and no special treatment — apart from a bit of support and reassurance — is required unless symptoms are severe.
>
> *Think PMS and then exaggerate it one hundred-fold. Think hormones on party drugs while riding a roller coaster. Think agitation, irritation, anger followed by uncontrolled weeping — all in response to your partner asking if you would like a cup of coffee.*

If symptoms surface within weeks of the birth, as is common, postnatal anxiety and depression can be mistaken for the baby blues.

There are distinct differences however, with respect to:

- **time** — with postnatal anxiety and depression symptoms will persist for longer than two weeks.
- **severity of symptoms** — with postnatal anxiety and depression mood changes are accompanied by feelings of guilt and hopelessness. There will be 'no light at the end of the tunnel'.
- **impact on the family** — without proper treatment, postnatal anxiety and depression will start affecting family life and a mother's ability to care for her child.

It's possible for women to develop postnatal anxiety and depression any time in the first year after giving birth, although usually it occurs in the first few months after delivery. Onset can be abrupt or gradual. For some women the baby blues just never go away.

For many women, anxiety symptoms will be the most obvious sign that something is wrong; some may even reject the label of 'postnatal depression' as a result. Phobias, panic disorders and obsessive compulsive disorder can all occur during this time.

Some women may experience posttraumatic stress symptoms, whilst others will even develop *posttraumatic stress disorder* as a consequence of a particularly difficult delivery; for example, one associated with severe pain, or a fear of losing her baby or her life. Alternatively, the emotional times surrounding birth may trigger memories of another traumatic experience earlier in life.

> *With an already fragile mental state I was dealing with intrusive, repetitive, disturbing thoughts. Day and night I could not rid these from my mind. Many years later I was diagnosed with posttraumatic stress disorder although at the time I thought I was going totally mad. I kept trying to 'debrief' but the thoughts never left me, intruding significantly into my daytime hours and causing further sleep deprivation at night. Although I mentioned this to a few people, including professionals, no-one actually had a conversation with me about them.*

There are lots of myths about postnatal anxiety and depression that persist to this day. Unfortunately it's not 'all due to hormones' and usually these conditions will not spontaneously go away with time. Nor, despite the cynical view of some, is it just a complaint of wealthy, middle-class women who are having trouble adjusting to the demands and restrictions that come with a new baby. In fact, postnatal depression is completely democratic: affecting first-time mums and experienced mums, teenage mums and older mums, and women from all socioeconomic backgrounds and cultures. Postnatal depression can also occur in men, and we discuss this further in Chapter 9.

As we mentioned earlier, there are some more serious mental health issues that can complicate pregnancy and the postnatal period. We asked Professor Marie-Paule Austin, Perinatal Psychiatrist and St John of God Chair of Perinatal and Women's Mental Health Unit at the University of NSW, to describe these conditions:

Bipolar disorder — also known as manic-depressive disorder — is marked by major swings in mood from elevated (or manic) to depressed. Mania is associated with increased energy and activity, reduced need for sleep, racing thoughts, grandiose ideas or plans, overconfidence in one's capacities, and loss of judgement (eg overspending, promiscuity or excess argumentativeness). At its most severe it can be associated with *psychotic* symptoms. Long-term medication is required for management of bipolar disorder. A woman with pre-existing bipolar disorder is much more likely to relapse in the early postnatal period, especially if she has ceased her medication and becomes very sleep deprived. The depressive episodes seen in bipolar disorder are usually much more common than the manic episodes and may be more severe than the depressive episodes not part of bipolar disorder. They are not uncommonly associated with significant suicidal thoughts or plans.

Puerperal psychosis is marked by sudden onset, usually in the first month after birth, of severe disturbance of behaviour, mood and thinking. Thinking becomes illogical and irrational (delusions) and this may be associated with auditory hallucinations (hearing voices).

Both bipolar disorder and puerperal psychosis make it almost impossible for a mother to care for her infant or function independently in any way; these mothers usually require admission to hospital for medication and 24-hour nursing, preferably with the infant so as to avoid separation and to provide supervision and a safe environment for the baby. Both conditions respond very well to medication ie antipsychotics and mood stabilisers (eg lithium) (see page 126).

Postnatal anxiety and depression — what does it look like?

It can be extremely difficult for a mother to gauge her feelings. When she is busy with a new baby, feeling tired and emotional, it can be hard to determine if her feelings are 'normal' or an indication of something more significant. (health professional)

Disturbed sleep, tiredness, loss of libido and worries about the baby can be symptoms of postnatal anxiety and depression but they are also the province of almost all new mothers. How do we distinguish between an otherwise healthy mum who is sleep deprived and stressed about an unsettled baby, and a woman who is experiencing postnatal anxiety and depression? The following list may help:

- low mood, sometimes described as a feeling of 'numbness' or being lost in a 'dark place' or 'fog'
- a loss of interest in activities previously enjoyed, such as socialising, sex or exercise
- a sense of complete loss of identity and self-worth
- a lack of joy in mothering — many mothers will still feel close to their baby despite their symptoms, but some women may be so depressed that they struggle to connect with their child
- sadness and tearfulness for no apparent reason
- exhaustion
- feelings of guilt especially guilt about being 'a bad mum'
- a loss of self-esteem, making women oversensitive to criticism
- concentration and memory problems — forgetting words mid-sentence; being unable to problem-solve
- an inability to make even the simplest decisions, such as what to have for dinner
- non-coping in someone who was a former 'coper' — even mundane tasks such as household chores and shopping becoming too much
- wanting to 'run away', wishing 'not to be alive', or even thoughts of death or suicide (see page 44)

I find it hard not to focus on my daughter. I feel like I have no life outside her, like there is nothing to me, other than 'mother'. I feel like in becoming a mother, I've lost my identity.

I came home early as I had what the hospital considered an easy birth. In hindsight I felt overwhelmed and wanted to be in my own environment and I felt judged by the midwives as I couldn't get the hang of breastfeeding. I was also tired, so I thought that I would be better at home... I am a very strong person by nature so it was strange to feel so out of my depth.

The worst times were when I did get a bit of a break, like when my three year old was out at daycare or with a friend. Instead of relaxing or enjoying time with the baby I would just lie on the bed and howl my eyes out when my baby slept or watched me or cried himself. I was desperate for a break but then couldn't do anything but cry.

On the inside, I feel numb and detached from life. I feel like I am going insane. I feel empty. I feel sad that I don't feel I am coping. I feel angry and disappointed that none of our family will help us with babysitting even though we beg them to.

However, some common symptoms may be less obvious:
- irritability and anger — snapping and yelling at partners and other loved ones for no reason
- being oversensitive to noise
- physical symptoms such as stomach cramps, headache or backache, without any apparent cause; women may visit their doctor several times with such complaints whilst the real problem remains undiscovered
- loss of appetite and weight loss; but for some women, overeating and weight gain
- being careless about grooming and appearance (although not always — some women will try desperately to keep up appearances)

- sleeping difficulties — either wanting to sleep all the time; or being unable to sleep, even when the baby is settled (early morning waking, before the baby, is common).

Other symptoms are those we might associate with anxiety:
- being continually on edge about everything
- repeated fears or negative thoughts, eg about germs and cleanliness, or somehow hurting the baby (even though the mother has no intention of doing this), or her partner being injured or leaving her
- constant worry about the baby — checking the baby is breathing throughout the night, or taking the baby to the doctor too often with imagined health complaints
- fear of being alone with the baby — needing to go out, or have a companion at home, all the time
- in contrast, some women develop a fear of going out and withdraw socially from family and friends
- panic attacks (see page 31).

Anxiety and depression… often respond to similar treatment. It is not unusual for them to co-exist, for example a woman who feels in despair and also constantly anxious about her ability to parent. (health professional)

Sometimes it feels like my head is going to explode because of all the worry I feel about my daughter. What if she hasn't eaten enough today? Is she gaining enough weight? Have I read enough books to her today? Her teeth look like they are going a bit yellow, what if they get rotten and fall out? Is she eating enough meat/dairy etc? Is she getting enough vitamin D each day from the sun? I wonder if she is supposed to be talking more than this for her age? How come she isn't walking yet etc? Basically, constant stress, constant worry, constant consuming thoughts about my daughter. That's the anxiety.

I considered the many ways that there could be an accident. Always an accident — a terrible accident. My most common thought was suffocation — a cot death — no one would know that I was such a bad mother. Everyone would instead comfort and support me. These were such frequent thoughts I don't believe I realised how extreme they really were.

I was much more anxious than depressed. I could always get out of bed and I usually had enough energy. But I felt it was impossible to keep the anxiety under control. I would feel like screaming all the time.

Do these stories remind you of anyone you know? Maybe even yourself? Remember that not **all** mothers will experience **all** of these symptoms, and severity will vary from one woman to the next.

If you believe you may be experiencing postnatal anxiety and depression it is vitally important to seek professional help. Wishing it away isn't going to be enough. If left untreated, postnatal depression can start affecting your relationship with your baby, as well as your partner and other family members; it can also increase your risk of developing longer term depression. Admitting you have a problem does not mean you are a 'failure'; you will be doing the best thing for your baby and yourself. The sooner you start getting the right treatment, the sooner you can start imagining a happier future, the one you deserve to have.

First things first — keeping safe

I believed that I would feel like this for the rest of my life — this was the new way to experience life as a mother — therefore a short life would be the best. I considered the different ways I could end my life, often while I was sitting, rocking back and forth weeping, on the kitchen floor.

No-one likes talking about suicide but it's essential we do, as too many women with perinatal depression have already taken their own lives. Sadly Australia's Gidget Foundation is named in memory of such a young woman: **www.gidgetfoundation.com.au**
To the outsider suicide seems unthinkable, so how can a woman reach this point?

As Shoshana Bennett explains, women with postnatal depression often have a strong desire to escape, and a very few — because of their disordered thinking — feel so 'worthless' that they assume their family won't miss them for long.[1] Of course, nothing could be further from the truth; suicide always leaves behind a trail of devastation, as loved ones struggle to comprehend what went wrong.

Therefore, if you are having thoughts of harming yourself or your baby — especially if you have an actual plan — you need to **get help immediately**. Contact your doctor or local emergency department, or call Lifeline's 24-hour counselling service **13 11 14**. The Suicide Call Back Service **1300 659 467** also provides crisis counselling across Australia, 24 hours per day 7 days a week.

3
HOW DID THIS HAPPEN?

I thought because I was an educated, professional woman that it wouldn't happen to me. I thought I was just tired and stressed but eventually it was obvious that things weren't right when I started having panic attacks and suffering ongoing chronic anxiety symptoms… I was crying all the time, scared to be alone with the baby.

In our society she goes home, her partner returns to work and she is left with a newborn baby. There is limited social interaction, sleep deprivation and an overwhelming sense of responsibility to care for her baby. Breastfeeding may be difficult. She may be sore as a result of the birth and find herself isolated and alone. (health professional)

It wasn't what I expected and it took me ages to realise that there really was something wrong. It wasn't just a case of 'poor me', or 'why me', but how the hell did we all come to be in this situation? You want explanations and reasons, you hope that these will give you some ways to help yourself get better. Maybe we all need to know the reasons for our depression or anxiety so that we can forgive ourselves and move on.

When you consider how ill-prepared many of us are for parenthood, we probably all have the potential to develop perinatal anxiety and depression in the right — or rather wrong — circumstances. In spite of the all the mythology surrounding motherhood, it doesn't come naturally to most of us. Like so many things that are difficult, you have to learn on the job.

Having said that, there are precipitating factors that do put a woman at greater risk. These *risk factors*, many and varied, are described below.

GENETIC OR BIOLOGICAL FACTORS

A genetic predisposition to anxiety and/or depressive disorders

If you have family members who have been treated for these conditions, or any other mental illness, you may be at higher risk of becoming ill during the perinatal period. Recent research suggests that postnatal depression may run in families. One study found the sisters of women who developed postnatal depression within two months of delivery were at greater risk of developing postnatal depression themselves.[1]

At the time I had my postnatal depression, my mother did admit that she and her mother experienced similar things, but that it was 'not spoken about' at that time.

It sorts of runs in my family. My mum tried to commit suicide when she was at home with us. I'm a twin. There was a severe stigma attached to it then and she was severely depressed.

Growing up in my family, we never really discussed mental health issues and certainly didn't talk about the dysfunctional behaviour which was all around us kids. So depression and anxiety were never really part of my vocabulary and it took me ages to accept them in myself, then about three seconds to see how widespread they are in my family. There are great genes too in my family, lots of good things, but definitely we have the anxiety and depression ones in there.

Hormonal sensitivity

Women who develop perinatal depression don't appear to have abnormal levels of pregnancy hormones, as originally supposed. However, there is research to suggest they may be extra sensitive to the normal changes in oestrogen and progesterone levels that occur during and after pregnancy, especially the big drop in these hormones that takes place shortly after delivery.[2] Women with a history of severe premenstrual tension (PMS) also appear to be a greater risk of postnatal depression, possibly because these women are very sensitive to hormone changes.

I had always suffered from PMS, then I had postnatal depression after having my first child. This was never diagnosed and that ultimately ended up with a marriage breakdown.

PSYCHOLOGICAL FACTORS

A past history of anxiety and depression

Women who have experienced depression, anxiety or another mental health disorder, whether associated with an earlier pregnancy or not, are at high risk of developing anxiety and depression during pregnancy and/or the postnatal period. In this scenario the perinatal mood disorder may be considered a *recurrence* of a previous illness, exacerbated rather than specifically caused by pregnancy and childbirth.

> *I had depression before my baby was born. I was on antidepressants before even falling pregnant (following the suicide of my dad). I knew I would be at high risk for postnatal depression.*

> **I feel that many people I see probably have an underlying undiagnosed anxiety disorder/personality issue and that the volatility of the perinatal period increases their anxiety symptoms and results in depression. Anxiety can precede depression and does on many occasions. (health professional)**

If a woman becomes anxious and depressed during her pregnancy she is at particularly high risk of developing postnatal depression after the baby is born.

> *I was screened by the Early Childhood Centre nurse using the standard short multiple choice test. As I already suffered from depression (during the pregnancy) I was very conscious of getting postnatal depression.*

A history of abuse or neglect

Women who have suffered physical, sexual or emotional abuse, and/or parental neglect, are particularly vulnerable to perinatal depression. Sometimes they may even use alcohol and drugs to mask unresolved emotional problems.

> *I think my postnatal depression experience was triggered by deep emotional wounds from childhood. It was not a hole, it was a chasm. Would better antenatal checks have caught me in a safety net? Maybe? I could have covered it up!*

> **My childhood absolutely had an influence. I was not mothered.**

SOCIAL FACTORS

Lack of support

Women who lack support, whether practical (such as someone doing the chores) or emotional (someone to confide in) are at risk of perinatal anxiety and depression. In Western societies like Australia, new parents are usually discharged from hospital within a day or two of the birth and left to sink or swim with little community support. Often we live a long way from family and loved ones, adding to our sense of isolation. The burden can be especially great for women living in rural and remote communities.

The medical profession has too often failed to work cooperatively with our midwifery colleagues and together I think that we have left a huge hole in the care of our patients. We care intensively antenatally, give one-on-one attention during delivery and supervise, nurture and educate during a brief postnatal stay. Then we send new parents home without support, without guidance. And then we wonder why it sometimes falls apart. (health professional)

There's the disappointment that my mother-in-law will not babysit our daughter despite being retired, living ten mins away, being in good health and having plenty of free time. I find it tremendously depressing whenever my girlfriends mention in conversation that their parents or in-laws babysit their kids weekly. I can only dream. Sigh.

Many of the mums I see in my practice don't have much support in terms of family nearby or friends with children. (health professional)

Cultural isolation

Recently-arrived immigrants and refugees are particularly vulnerable at this time, as language barriers and cultural differences make it especially hard for them to navigate the health system. In some cultures women may even face family disapproval for seeking help. Refugees may be already suffering posttraumatic stress disorders and grief resulting from separation from their country and loved ones.

Aboriginal and Torres Strait Islander women lose more children to infant mortality, and by having them taken into care, than non-Indigenous women. They also appear to be at increased risk of perinatal mental health problems. However, language barriers, suspicion of alien birth practices, and fear of family separations mean Indigenous women may feel reluctant to admit to parenting difficulties.[3]

To help address cultural and language barriers, *beyondblue* has produced its educational booklet *Emotional Health during Pregnancy and Early Parenthood* in 20 different languages. **www.beyondblue.org.au/index. aspx?link_id=7.980#Postnatal**

The NSW Multicultural Health Communication Service has also produced a booklet called, *Sad feelings after childbirth —- a 'hidden' problem* in many different languages.
www.mhcs.health.nsw.gov.au/publication_details/5925.asp

Poor personal relationships

Single mothers, or those with an unsupportive or abusive partner, are at particularly high risk of depression. Those with a troubled relationship with their own mother are also more likely to experience postnatal depression, and sometimes this is especially the case when they have a daughter themselves.

My husband didn't mean to be useless, but he was worse than useless. I think he made me worse. It was a hard time for him too because he was trying to get settled into a new career here and make a good impression. He never, ever took a day off to help me and he used to work a lot at weekends. I felt totally abandoned.

He used to say those terrible clichéd things like: 'Can't you just pull yourself together?' 'Why can't you just get on with it?' He himself couldn't manage our toddler and the baby together and yet he totally expected me to be able to. He never came to the doctor. He didn't read up on depression. He refused to go to counselling for a long, long time. My husband's not a bad person — not at all — just not good at dealing with a wife who was not coping at all.

I see postnatal women who were previously excelling in their career and now feeling out of control after birth, in their 30's; they often don't have good relationship with their own mum. (health professional)

Financial worries

Women from low income families are especially susceptible, although all of us can suffer money worries. Big mortgage repayments may force some women to return to work earlier than they would wish to, creating new anxieties about childcare, and juggling work and parenthood.

There were other factors too, like financial issues, pain with pregnancy, my teenager being difficult and the previous postnatal depression.

Teenage mothers

Teen mothers are at higher risk of perinatal anxiety and depression.

Young mums are often unprepared for motherhood and commonly have no partner to support them emotionally and financially. In most cultures, teenagers are not at the most appropriate developmental stage for taking on parenthood.

Stressful life events

Some stressful events, such as the death of a loved one or job loss, are clearly unavoidable. It is very difficult to build a new bond with your baby when you are grieving the loss of another important relationship. However, it is not a good idea to renovate or move house a few months either side of giving birth, although an amazing percentage of people will do so — for obvious reasons.

> *My father was dying of cancer, and he did not have a granddaughter and was desperate for my child to be a girl and to live to see the baby. He died when my daughter was nine months old, I had never lost anyone close to me before that time and my husband was not very happy in his job.*

PERSONALITY FACTORS

'Anxious worrier' types

Women who have low self-esteem and negative thinking patterns appear more susceptible to perinatal anxiety and depression.

'Perfectionist' personality types

Whilst good organisational skills and attention to detail are rewarded in the workplace, parenthood requires a more easygoing, go-with-the flow attitude. Perfectionists, who are sometimes driven to perfectionism by underlying anxiety issues, can struggle to adjust, and may get depressed and anxious as a consequence.

I would say there was immediate anxiety there, just in the way that I'm a first time mum, I don't have a mum of my own, and I'm a perfectionist so I have high standards for myself, I guess.

I see mums who have had a career before having kids and are often in their 30s and used to being in control. Motherhood feels chaotic for some of these women and they worry about being incompetent, a feeling they are not used to. (health professional)

PREGNANCY-RELATED FACTORS

Unwanted pregnancy

Unfortunately not all babies arrive at the most convenient time. Teenagers, single mothers, mothers with money worries, older mothers who thought they had 'finished' their families and women who already have a young baby to care for, can all find themselves pregnant.

Fertility issues

Conversely, problems conceiving and the use of IVF also increase vulnerability to anxiety and depression. The rollercoaster ride beforehand, hormone injections, anxieties during the pregnancy and — for some — an emotional letdown after the baby arrives, may all contribute.

A difficult pregnancy

Complications such as bleeding, diabetes and high blood pressure, can make pregnancy an anxious time; there may be worries about the baby's health, intrusive tests and treatments, and in some cases the need for hospitalisation.

A 'bad' experience of childbirth

If things don't go according to plan (eg an emergency caesarean or complications) women may blame themselves and/or nursing and medical staff for their perceived 'failure'. In worst-case scenarios, acute or longer-term PTSD can result.

I find that PTSD is another frequently missed condition in the postnatal period and that women need the opportunity to debrief about their birth experience. Insufficient pain relief during labour is a large contributing factor to this as is an unexpected outcome and the loss of control the woman feels. (health professional)

Previous pregnancy loss

Unresolved issues from previous stillbirth or miscarriage will frequently surface in a new pregnancy.

I had no anxiety or depression during the pregnancy, but deep grief from a previous miscarriage.

BABY-RELATED FACTORS

Losing a baby to stillbirth, miscarriage or early neonatal death

Postnatal anxiety and depression commonly occur when there is no baby left to hold. This particularly distressing situation is discussed further in Chapter 10.

Twins (or triplets)

As we discuss further in Chapter 10, the relentless demands of caring for more than one baby can become too much for some mothers.

I loved motherhood the first time round. I remember thinking that this is my calling in life; motherhood is what I was made for. I don't know if I set myself up for a really big fall with the twins.

You know what it's like with twins. You never have one second, not one second downtime, when where you feel you have got things under control. The boy twin wasn't a sleeper, he just wanted to be up and to be cuddled so I had him in a sling almost the entire time, it was the only way I could get him to sleep, so I'd be cooking in a sling, changing nappies in a sling.

I went from loving motherhood to absolutely hating motherhood. I was resenting the twins and I didn't want that.

A baby that is 'colicky', difficult to settle and sleeps poorly

Sleep deprivation is a risk factor for postnatal depression.

Shock was the main thing I remember. This was a very unsettled baby, even the hospital commented, and the sleep deprivation, I had never done anything this hard in my whole life. It seemed like there was no end in sight! We ended up getting a maternity nurse in the second week so we could get some sleep. She had worked with babies for over ten years and also found my baby daughter very unsettled, but she was very supportive and a real lifeline.

I can remember being so tired and wondering what I was doing wrong, because the baby was always so unsettled, and seem to be more settled with other people, which made me feel worse. It felt like it would never end and the sleep deprivation was like nothing I have ever (or since) felt.

A baby with health issues

Giving birth to a baby with significant health issues, such as prematurity, or a disability, for example, Down syndrome, can provoke overwhelming feelings of guilt and anxiety. Once again, these circumstances deserve more discussion (see Chapter 10).

Breastfeeding problems

Women for whom breastfeeding is a struggle often feel they have 'failed' as mothers.

> *Babies are sometimes unsettled and have feeding issues. Mums are sometimes struggling with breastfeeding. (health professional)*

> ***The birth was easy but breastfeeding was terrible and I had so much pressure from everyone to breastfeed — so after a month when my milk still hadn't come in I gave up — I was breastfeeding, expressing and topping up on three hours' sleep a night.***

Having a baby of the 'unwanted' gender

Many of us would like to have a choice when it comes to the gender of our babies. Unfortunately nature isn't always so obliging.

> *He was meant to be a girl. I found out whilst I was pregnant and cried and cried. Then I felt like an awful mum because I was being disloyal to the two gorgeous little boys I already had. It was only at an antenatal visit, when the obstetrician for a brief period couldn't detect a heartbeat, that I realised I still wanted my baby boy.*

With such an exhaustive list of psychological, social and baby-related risk factors, it would be a rare woman who could not relate to at least one. However, risk factors are just that: whilst they increase your chance of developing a condition, they do not inevitably predict you will (eg smoking increases the risk of developing heart disease and cancer, but not every smoker develops heart disease or cancer). Genes and environment are both important. Some women may have identifiable risk factors yet experience no anxiety and depression, whereas — as a study in New Zealand found — it's possible to have no obvious social risk factors for postnatal depression yet still succumb.[4] Ultimately we need to remember that depression is for many a biological illness, susceptible to changing hormone levels and alterations in brain 'chemistry' (see page 47). Therefore, if you are experiencing symptoms you do not need to make excuses, what you do need to do is get some help.

4
EARLY
INTERVENTION

Antenatal and postnatal screening have both been found to be invaluable for detecting women at risk. These initial screening interviews and questionnaires aim to detect women who need further assessment and are usually not intended be used in isolation to diagnose a condition like antenatal or postnatal depression or anxiety. (health professional)

I should have asked for help sooner but I didn't realise that what I had was postnatal depression. I also had this crazy idea that I should just deal with it and get on with my life and if I just woke up, got out of bed each day and got through the day that that was another day closer to becoming 'normal' again. I should not have functioned like that... I still have little or no memory of the first 12 months of my twins' life.

I think screening can be of benefit, however, like all things it is not going to catch all people, nor will all people want to discuss these issues with the person conducting the screening. I do feel

it is important to raise awareness of these issues with women
and to plant the seed in order to help women recognise the
importance of their mental health and wellbeing at this time
and that it is of equal importance as one's physical health.
(health professional)

WHY WE NEED SCREENING

Pregnancy and the first few months of motherhood can be, and often are, surreal: it's not only first time mothers who might feel this. Subsequent pregnancies and babies can completely change the family dynamics, upsetting routines and disrupting emotions. Not so long ago it was thought that pregnancy was a protective time for mental health.[1] However, it is now believed that perhaps more than 10% of pregnant women experience anxiety and depression and what's more, up to 40% of mothers diagnosed with postnatal depression experienced depression while they were pregnant.[2] (See Chapter 2).

Reminder

Generally speaking, if a mother is experiencing intense feelings that are impacting negatively on her life and lasting for two weeks or more, this is the time to seek professional help. This is not a diagnosis of anxiety and depression but it is an indication that the mother could do with some help and support.

Pregnancy can bring with it all sorts of unexpected physical and emotional surprises which may have significant impact on our mental wellbeing. Motherhood is a role we have no real training for: the job description keeps changing, each day can find you mentally and physically exhausted, yet wondering what it is exactly that you have achieved. Many mothers have very little idea what to do with their baby in those early weeks (who can honestly tell if it's a cry because of hunger, boredom or the desire for a cuddle?). Then there's sleep deprivation, messing with your mind.

Each pregnancy and baby, whether it's our first or our fourth, can cause havoc in different ways. Babies are individuals and we respond to them differently, depending on our circumstances and their personalities. Most mothers, even the happy and contented ones, would admit that all is not perfect all of the time. Every mother does experience at least some moment of doubt or confusion during the first few months of their babies' lives.

> *Is it normal... to spend your day in your pyjamas, to wonder how the house got into such a ransacked state, suddenly realising at 6pm that there is no food for dinner... to feel so overwhelmed you just don't know where to start... to wonder how to respond to your partner's incredulous 'what have you been doing all day' question and wonder that yourself...*

> **I suppose it can be tricky to get an accurate diagnosis. I don't get too hung up on this. I can see if they are depressed or anxious and work with that rather than trying to be 100% sure of the diagnosis. (health professional)**

No wonder perinatal mood disorders are so difficult to diagnose. The physical discomforts of pregnancy can be obvious and sometimes difficult to cope with. In addition, most women will also experience a range of emotions during this time. This is normal. However, pregnancy is also a time when some women, for a host of reasons, may develop anxiety and depression (see Chapter 3).

After the baby is born, most of us could easily tick off a number of the classic symptoms on a list... sleep deprivation (do you need to ask?)... change in eating patterns (when the only food to be found in the house is a packet of Tim Tams?)... confused thoughts (how am I supposed to think or feel when I have no reference points?). Yet these symptoms do not necessarily mean a new mother is unwell. The best indications of how a mother is really getting on can be gleaned through a discussion about feelings and mood.

Background to the current system

The Federal Government is currently funding a project for universal antenatal screening for perinatal mental health across Australia.[3] This program commenced in 2001 and is being implemented over time in public hospitals in some form or other across the country. It has not yet been implemented in the private hospitals, which means that around 30% of pregnant women in Australia do not receive this antenatal screening.

> *I didn't really realise, at least initially, that what I was experiencing was depression or something similar. It was only as I came out of the fog, and even now looking back, that I realise how badly I was functioning as a human being let alone as a mother.*

> **Antenatally I was screened by the maternal nurse — she picked up that things weren't right, and I completed the Edinburgh score. Anyway the good thing was my maternal health nurse suggested I join a postnatal depression support group and see a counsellor.**

> *Screening in and of itself is not the answer to the problem, however, it is an important tool. If people can be identified and treated earlier in the piece then it has served well. It has been criticised for providing too many false positives... better that than not picking women up and missing an opportunity to raise a person's awareness of the importance of good mental health. (health professional)*

Why screen for antenatal and/or postnatal anxiety and depression?[3]

- Perinatal (antenatal/postnatal) anxiety and depression affects around 16% of women during this period. There are significant long-term impacts on women's mental health and parenting, on their partners and on the developmental prospects of their children.

- Prevention does not appear effective, nevertheless screening provides an opportunity to prevent vulnerable women from slipping into illness. It is not really possible to predict who will experience anxiety and depression. Although there are a number of known stress factors that can influence how a mother feels (see Chapter 3), their presence in her life does not necessarily mean she will experience anxiety and depression. Conversely women with no apparent stressors can still experience anxiety and depression. Early intervention, with best-practice, *evidenced-based* treatments, offers the best outcome.

- Routine screening gives the best possible opportunity to ensure that over half of the women that would be otherwise missed will be identified.

- Identification alone does not ensure treatment will be sought. It must be combined with staff education, support and facilitation of pathways to care (see page 69).

- Providing information during pregnancy enables women to be better informed about mental health issues. When given information, women at risk of depression were better able to assess their own mood and levels of anxiety. These women reported better satisfaction with the care they received and the services they were referred to when compared with women who were not screened.

The model for screening in Australia is for pregnant women to be screened sometime during their first trimester (often at the booking in appointment at around 11–12 weeks). Mothers will then be screened postnatally through the Early Childhood Health Centre. We need to emphasise that this is a model and is not always reflected in everyday clinical practice. The screening usually involves an interview with a trained midwife or nurse who administers two questionnaires — the Edinburgh Postnatal Depression Scale (EPDS), together with a much broader questionnaire known as a *psychosocial assessment*.

These questionnaires are easily obtainable and are used by health professionals in many settings, such as the trained midwife or nurse at the hospital antenatal clinic, the nurse at the early childhood centre, or the GP.

The EPDS was developed in 1987 and is used around the world. It is known as a *validated screening tool* and is used to obtain an indication of whether a mother may be suffering from depression. It was initially developed to be used postnatally (hence its name) but is now regularly used in an antenatal setting.[4] (As a result, some professionals now refer to the EPDS simply as the Edinburgh Depression Scale (EDS). It has also been used successfully to screen fathers. It includes a set of ten questions which the mother reads and answers. The health professional then scores the mother's answers.

The EPDS is reproduced on page 73. It is also available to download from the *beyondblue* website. Follow the links through the Postnatal Depression tag.

beyondblue advise that if your score is ten points or above, you should speak to a health professional about your symptoms. However, it's important to note that scores are only a rough guide as to whether someone potentially has depression and anxiety.

Ideally, the EPDS should be administered by a trained health professional, as part of a broader psychosocial assessment (see below).

There are many examples of psychosocial assessment questionnaires in use around the country. They vary in length and in the questions that are asked — some are validated, others are not — but their main task is to give a broader picture of what is going on in a mother's life at this time. The psychosocial assessment is conducted as an interview. It usually includes questions on physical and emotional health, any past history of depression, recent stressful events, the woman's relationship with her partner, her childhood, her support networks and personality type. The interview might also include questions regarding drug and alcohol use and domestic violence. Many of the questions are open-ended and give mothers the opportunity to talk freely about themselves and how they are feeling.

General practitioners, obstetricians, psychologists, psychiatrists, social workers and child and family health nurses as well as midwives are able to administer these questionnaires. Ideally, health professionals should undertake training before administering either of these questionnaires, in order for them to assess the results and identify patients correctly. Trained health professionals should also have access to good referral resources and networks.

It is really important to remember that these tools are both screening, not diagnostic, questionnaires. They are, however, very helpful in providing an indication of the state of the mother's emotional health, particularly when used in conjunction with each other. The psychosocial assessment adds much needed context to the EPDS.

HOW THE SCREENING PROGRAM SHOULD WORK

With the EPDS, it's so obvious what you are supposed to write, you could blitz that and you can hide it, hide it from yourself even. I knew the answers I was supposed to give and I gave them.

'If only' someone had given me the time and had thought to ask the right questions... and then to listen. The horrible months I spent feeling anxious and spiralling into deeper depression might never have occurred. I was desperate to talk to a health professional but I was in no position to open the conversation myself.

I did lie to the early childhood nurse at first when doing the EPDS. I was scared to admit the truth in case they thought I was an unfit mum and took my baby away. It sounds crazy now but when I was depressed it made sense to lie as I didn't know or trust that nurse, and she had very little time to spend with me and bub.

Screening for perinatal anxiety and depression is now being carried out routinely in most public hospitals and early childhood centres around Australia. It is a standardised interview and generally includes the EPDS and a psychosocial assessment. But remember — these questionnaires are used for screening, not diagnosis.

Antenatally — in the public hospital antenatal clinic a trained midwife conducts a one-hour interview during an early antenatal visit (often at the booking-in clinic). Some hospital protocols also include a second antenatal screening interview at around 28 weeks. This second interview is often much shorter and just includes the administering of the EPDS. It does, however, provide pregnant women with another opportunity to discuss any issues they may have.

Postnatally — a trained child and family health nurse conducts a one hour interview, generally in the home. This should occur at the first postnatal visit, usually at around 6–8 weeks. For private patients this may be the first time they are in fact screened.

An Important Message

These questionnaires provide opportunities for mothers to voice any concerns they may have about their feelings and mood. There should be enough time during the interview to talk about issues that may be causing distress and thoughts that may be disturbing you.

As you can see from the quotes above, some mothers talk of 'cheating' on the EPDS. It is easy to answer this questionnaire in any way you would like to. If you do not want the health professional to know how you are really feeling, it is not difficult to hide your true feelings by providing the answers you think might be 'correct'. However, if you are feeling vulnerable or needy or anxious it really is in your best interest to share these feelings with a health professional.

If, however, you do not connect with this particular health professional you may want to consider speaking to another professional that you do trust. There is help available for mothers who are experiencing adjustment issues or who are anxious and/or depressed. The sooner you receive good help, the sooner you will start to feel better.

Is antenatal and postnatal mental health screening a good thing?

The short answer is yes. Research over the last few years does provisionally support this answer. There are many reasons why health professionals feel very positive about screening all women both during pregnancy and after their babies are born.

- Pregnant women and mothers appear to be very comfortable with the questions asked and the manner in which they are asked.[5]
- Screening leads to an increase in awareness of anxiety and depression during this period for mothers, fathers and the

general community.

- Screening provides mothers with an opportunity they might not otherwise have to talk about their feelings and concerns in a secure environment.
- Many mothers will be identified as needing help who otherwise would have passed unnoticed. Their anxiety and depression might then have a greater negative impact on themselves and their families.
- The earlier a woman receives help the smaller the impact is on her family and the sooner she will start to feel better.
- Unwell mothers can have impaired parenting and their young children can also experience emotional and cognitive problems. It is very important for young babies to develop a secure attachment to a main caregiver early in their lives. There is some evidence that mothers who are unwell can affect the quality of the relationship with, and cognitive development of, their children. (See page 111 for more information on Infant Attachment Theory.)
- There is some evidence that anxious and depressed pregnant women can have a negative impact on their unborn baby (see page 115). If this is identified and treated, the outcome for the mother and baby is improved.
- Antenatal screening should be seen as routine — just the same as the antenatal blood tests that most pregnant women have.
- Women are unlikely to attend the health professional already diagnosed or willing to discuss their feelings. They will often present with a concern regarding a baby or child. Screening provides a unique opportunity for mothers such as these to be assessed and to talk about their feelings.
- While, generally speaking, anxiety and depression are difficult to predict, screening and assessment can be used to help prevent or at least ameliorate some of the symptoms. If risk factors are identified in a mother and then successfully addressed she may avoid the full severity of anxiety and depression.

Are there any reasons why screening might cause problems?

Certainly, there can be 'false positives' with screening. Some women will be identified who don't require extra help (they might have just had a very hard two weeks at the time of screening and their issues resolve over time). Re-screening for less symptomatic women, or a follow-up detailed clinical assessment can help with correct diagnosis. Often women who have had a difficult time appreciate someone hearing their story, even if things have improved. (health professional)

Sadly, screening can be done too routinely without really using our clinical judgment. It has a place as a universal primary tool but needs to be used within the context of clinical judgement. There is room for misuse or abuse if not used properly. (health professional)

If the screening is administered properly by a trained health professional it should be a positive experience which provides helpful information. However, we do not live in a perfect world and there are some examples where problems might occur.

- Women can choose to 'lie' or not fully disclose what is going on and, as a result, the presence of anxiety and depression will not be detected.
- The stigma of mental illness can influence the answers provided by some women.
- There is a possibility of false positives or false negatives — some women may be incorrectly diagnosed with anxiety and depression — particularly if the person administering the tool is not adequately trained or perhaps not sensitive enough to the context of a particular woman's life.
- Limited referral options can cause problems; women who are identified as needing help might not be able to receive the care they need.

- Screening can be incorrectly administered as a diagnostic tool rather than a screening tool.
- Some women may feel that the screening opens up a 'Pandora's box' they were quite happy to live with closed.
- Some medical professionals might feel inadequately trained to deal with the issues that screening might uncover.
- Some medical professionals may not have the time or the capacity to listen as a mother offloads.
- Anxiety can sometimes be diagnosed as depression, especially in the case of post traumatic stress disorder. Incorrect diagnosis can lead to incorrect treatment and slower recovery.

For women whose difficulties are continuing, screening can open doors for additional help in solving emotional and practical issues. (health professional)

PATHWAYS TO CARE

The care a mother receives will depend on where she and her family are living and her psychological and social circumstances. Cities have a number of resources with a variety of care options, while unfortunately in rural and regional areas obtaining further help can be rather hit and miss (see Resources Guide). Most mothers will be offered some form of counselling, and for some this will be accompanied by prescription medication. Mothers may also require practical help in settling or feeding their baby, support with other children, or help in finding childcare so they can have a few hours away from the family.

Perinatal anxiety and depression does not always occur in isolation. Some mothers may have underlying anxiety and depression issues and may already be under the care of a health professional. Other mothers may have a variety of issues going on; depression and anxiety can sometimes be associated with drug and alcohol abuse, personality problems, and/or relationship dysfunction.

If a midwife or child and family health nurse considers the mother to be in need of further assessment or assistance she may be referred back to her GP. The GP is in the unique position of being able to manage the many different aspects of help that might be required (see pages 88 and 113). Other referral pathways include intervention and care provided by hospital social workers, psychologists or psychiatrists. In some instances, where mothers have a variety of problems, they will be looked after by a multidisciplinary team of health professionals.

Some mothers can be referred to supported playgroups while others may obtain help from a variety of outpatient services. Some mothers might be referred to a mother/baby unit for specialised care as an inpatient. They may stay as an inpatient for a number of weeks depending on individual circumstances (see Chapter 6).

A small percentage of mothers may require urgent family help, particularly if they are experiencing financial problems or are living with domestic violence.

In any case, when the system works well, the health professional who administers the antenatal or postnatal screening will arrange for the ongoing care of any mother who is identified as requiring it.

WHAT ABOUT FATHERS?

Naively, I had thought the baby would just slot in and life would continue as before. But it didn't. My wife was always tired — I felt like we never had time to talk or cuddle or have some space to ourselves. And the baby was always crying, needing her, and I didn't know what to do. To make matters worse I was meant to be managing a big project at work, and started feeling anxious about that too — only I couldn't talk to my wife about it, because she had enough on her plate, and I couldn't sleep between the baby's squalling and worrying about work. I gave up my indoor cricket team so I could help out more at home but my wife and I just ended up snapping at each other. Soon I didn't want to go home at all. I felt like I'd lost my wife, I had a child I didn't like all that much and my life was over.

Those words were written by a father who was eventually diagnosed with postnatal depression. He was one of the lucky ones. He received the help he needed and recovered. Research suggests that around one in ten men will suffer from perinatal anxiety and/or depression, either in response to depression in their partner or as a result of their own personal situation (see Chapter 9). However, there is no screening program in place for fathers.

Fathers who are well may find it very difficult to understand what is happening to their partner. For this reason it is really important for health professionals to include fathers in any general discussions and treatment plans. Providing fathers with information and resources and practical ideas is also important. Fathers need support too.

Some small studies have looked at fathers and screening and these show that the EPDS seems to be well tolerated by men and is a useful screening tool for postnatal depression in men.[7] Unfortunately, with no formal screening program, it is often up to the father to seek help for himself, or hope that his condition is picked up through involvement with his partner's treatment. This means that anxiety and depression in new fathers often goes unreported and untreated. This, of course, can add stress to an already distressing situation.

EARLY INTERVENTION IN COMPLEX FAMILY SITUATIONS

It goes without saying that the more complex the domestic situation and the earlier the intervention, the better the outcome. Complex family situations are often dependent on a well mother to hold all the pieces together. If a mother is identified as having a number of contributing issues such as lack of social support, problems with drugs and alcohol or a violent relationship, it is likely that she and her family may be cared for by a number of professionals. These might include a psychologist, social worker, and an early childhood health nurse. Various support services or programs such as a family care centre may also be included in the mental health care plan (see Resources Guide).

Early intervention is the most effective way to help families who are struggling to stay together. Mothers, fathers and children may all benefit from a range of professional help. Struggling families who are not lucky enough to receive help and support in the early years often find that their complexities are compounded and family cohesion can easily unravel.

Early intervention is important

Most psychiatrists, doctors and allied health providers who work in this area believe that screening is an extremely important intervention. Antenatal and postnatal screening has been shown to be effective in identifying women with perinatal mood disorders. The earlier a diagnosis is made, the sooner help can be accessed and the faster the recovery. Mothers have such an important role to play in the family. A well mother is an asset to every family and the impact of a mother who is not well can be profound.

The women quoted below describe the feelings they had when they realised that something was not quite right. These feelings led them to seek help for their anxiety and depression and this help aided their recovery, enabling them to enjoy their motherhood.

When you cry for no reason or for lots of reasons... when lack of sleep makes life become too hard... when you start looking at the world through fuzzy eyes... when you start drinking to cope.

When there's no respite from feeling awful, nothing is funny, heartwarming or even makes you smile, when it all feels too hard and awful and never ending, when you cry and cry and

can't get it together, when you feel like hurting or damaging your child or yourself, when you feel no-one cares. Whenever you feel like it might not be ok, it's best to get help as soon as possible before it all goes wrong.

While having a baby and the early years of parenting can be really hard work, you should have fun too. If you find you can't laugh at yourself or at the crazy situations babies can lead you into you might have to consider that you could do with some professional help. Accessing help as soon as possible will mean a faster recovery for you and less trauma for all the family.

Edinburgh Postnatal Depression Scale 1 (EPDS)

Name: _____

Address: _____

Your Date of Birth: _____ Baby's Date of Birth: _____

Phone: _____

As you are pregnant or have recently had a baby, we would like to know how you are feeling. Please check the answer that comes closest to how you have felt **IN THE PAST 7 DAYS,** not just how you feel today.

Here is an example, already completed.

I have felt happy:

☐ Yes, all the time

☒ Yes, most of the time This would mean: "I have felt happy most of

☐ No, not very often the time" during the past week.

☐ No, not at all Please complete the other questions in the same way.

In the past 7 days:

1. I have been able to laugh and see the funny side of things

☐ As much as I always could

☐ Not quite so much now

☐ Definitely not so much now

☐ Not at all

*6. Things have been getting on top of me

☐ Yes, most of the time I haven't been able to cope at all

☐ Yes, sometimes I haven't been coping as well as usual

☐ No, most of the time I have coped quite well

☐ No, I have been coping as well as ever

2. I have looked forward with enjoyment to things
- ☐ As much as I ever did
- ☐ Rather less than I used to
- ☐ Definitely less than I used to
- ☐ Hardly at all

*3. I have blamed myself unnecessarily when things went wrong
- ☐ Yes, most of the time
- ☐ Yes, some of the time
- ☐ Not very often
- ☐ No, never

4. I have been anxious or worried for no good reason
- ☐ No, not at all
- ☐ Hardly ever
- ☐ Yes, sometimes
- ☐ Yes, very often

*5. I have felt scared or panicky for no very good reason
- ☐ Yes, quite a lot
- ☐ Yes, sometimes
- ☐ No, not much
- ☐ No, not at all

*7. I have been so unhappy that I have had difficulty sleeping
- ☐ Yes, most of the time
- ☐ Yes, sometimes
- ☐ Not very often
- ☐ No, not at all

*8. I have felt sad or miserable
- ☐ Yes, most of the time
- ☐ Yes, quite often
- ☐ Not very often
- ☐ No, not at all

*9. I have been so unhappy that I have been crying
- ☐ Yes, most of the time
- ☐ Yes, quite often
- ☐ Only occasionally
- ☐ No, never

*10. The thought of harming myself has occurred to me
- ☐ Yes, quite often
- ☐ Sometimes
- ☐ Hardly ever
- ☐ Never

Administered/Reviewed by

Date

1 Source: Cox, J.L., Holden, J.M., and Sagovsky, R. 1987. Detection of postnatal depression: Development of the 10-item

Edinburgh Postnatal Depression Scale. *British Journal of Psychiatry* 150:782-786 .

2 Source: K. L. Wisner, B. L. Parry, C. M. Piontek, Postpartum Depression N Engl J Med vol. 347, No 3, July 18, 2002,194-199

Psychosocial assessment — what exactly is it?

The psychosocial assessment helps to provide the health professional with some context to add more meaning to the EPDS. This assessment can take place antenatally, generally at the booking-in clinic at the maternity hospital, or postnatally, usually through the Early Childhood Centre.

Ideally, mothers should be asked these questions by a trained nurse or midwife in a conversational setting. This will encourage relaxed discussion and provide an opportunity for any concerns to be raised. The health professional should be sensitive to how the mother might be feeling, have good listening skills, and an ability to 'read between the lines'. It is very important for the nurse or midwife to have access to clear referral pathways that can be used if a mother needs to be offered further support.

There are a variety of psychosocial questionnaires that have been developed for use in Australia. While they range in length and scope, all the questionnaires are designed to create a broad picture of a mother's life. In most cases, mothers are very positive about the screening process, with some reporting that the extra attention they received gave them a feeling of added support.

The following list provides a general overview of the sorts of subjects that might be covered in a psychosocial assessment:

- **Age** of the mother
- **Obstetric history** — current and past problems, including infertility.
- **Health care** — clinic attendance, diet, exercise, lifestyle.
- **Pregnancy** — unplanned and/or unwanted.
- **Drug use** (alcohol, cigarettes, other) — past or present (patient herself or partner)
- **Social support** — perceived availability of practical **and** emotional support from partner, parents, other family, friends.
- **Personality** — self-esteem, anxiety, perfectionist or dependent traits.
- **Mental health** — current and/or previous problems of any

kind, for example stress, anxiety or depression.

- **Family mental health** — current or past problems or illness.
- **Bereavements** (recent or otherwise significant) — including miscarriage, termination, stillbirth or sudden infant death.
- **Childhood experiences** — positive or negative, including major separations, neglect, abuse.
- **Refugee or recent migrant status.**
- **Community status** — membership of a minority group.
- **Life events** — recent or long-standing stressors, including cultural issues, health, housing, finances, employment, language, isolation and related difficulties.

The authors would like to gratefully acknowledge Professor Bryanne Barnett for her professional contribution to information on psychosocial assessment.

5
DIAGNOSIS

I definitely resisted diagnosis, I was in denial. I thought because I was an educated, professional woman... that it wouldn't happen to me... eventually it was obvious that things weren't right when I started having panic attacks and suffering ongoing chronic anxiety symptoms... disturbing thoughts and dreams about the baby.

Personally I had no resistance [to diagnosis]... I was so acutely ill that I just wanted someone to make me feel better and if that meant being diagnosed with postnatal depression, then I did not care.

Diagnosis was the hardest part of my illness. I knew I was unwell but didn't know where to go for help.

In the previous chapter we discussed the importance of screening for perinatal anxiety and depression and the current state of affairs in Australia. However, screening is *not* the same thing as getting a diagnosis. Even if you have been asked to complete an Edinburgh Postnatal Depression Scale and scored in the 'at-risk' range, that does not necessarily mean you have perinatal mood disorder; further investigations are always required. This chapter briefly discusses the diagnostic process.

WHAT'S IN A NAME?

One of the challenges we've encountered while compiling this handbook is writing something that will meet the needs of all the women who might potentially benefit from it. As no two women's experiences of anxiety and depression are likely to be the same, so no two women will be arriving at this point with the same symptoms, biology, personality, history and life complications.

As we made clear in early on, the old label *postnatal depression* is no longer adequate. A one-size-fits-all terminology does not describe the experience of many women: those who develop symptoms before they've even had their baby, or those stricken with anxiety, who feel more stressed than 'depressed' (or at least what they understand by the term). Authorities are also concerned that women with severe mental health disorders such as puerperal psychosis (see page 39) may sometimes be incorrectly labelled as having 'postnatal depression', with potentially tragic consequences.[1]

But it goes further than that. Even if we leave aside more serious perinatal mental health disorders, and restrict our discussion to anxiety and depression, these conditions can still vary greatly in symptoms, severity and cause.

For many women perinatal anxiety and depression may be a temporary and very treatable condition. Prior to becoming pregnant these women may have been essentially happy and healthy but for a variety of reasons — perhaps because of an hormonal sensitivity or simply because of the unexpected stresses of pregnancy and motherhood — they become down and anxious. With the right sort of help these women may be restored to good health reasonably quickly.

However, some women will have a long personal history of anxiety and/or depression and for them pregnancy and childbirth may be exacerbating factors.

For others, 'ghosts' from their past (such as a background of childhood neglect) may resurface during these emotionally challenging times. Others may have additional health problems, an eating disorder, drug and alcohol problems, or simply a personality that predisposes them to anxiety or low moods.

Women with complex histories are likely to have a longer and more complicated road to recovery. That is not to say that recovery is not possible, just that it may take more assistance and time to get there.

DIAGNOSTIC POSSIBILITIES

Untangling what is anxiety/depression/adjustment etc can be tricky. An accurate diagnosis is essential if medication is to be a treatment option. (health professional)

The umbrella term *perinatal anxiety and depression* encompasses several different diagnoses.

We talked about the *Diagnostic and Statistical Manual of Mental Disorders, 4th edition — Text Revision* (DSM-IV-TR) in Chapter 2.[2] There is no specific diagnostic category for perinatal depression in the DSM-IV-TR so, if your symptoms are primarily those of depression, under the DSM-IV-TR you would generally be diagnosed with a *major depressive disorder* (refer to pages 30 and 40 for these symptoms).[3]

Other potential DSM-IV-TR diagnoses include the anxiety disorders discussed on page 31: generalised anxiety disorder, phobia, obsessive compulsive disorder, PTSD and panic disorder. As we've discussed earlier, however, this is not necessarily an either/or situation — whilst it's possible you may be diagnosed with a stand-alone anxiety disorder, such as PTSD, in practice this happens relatively rarely. A recent Australian study in postnatal women found that, even if anxiety symptoms are present, it's more common for a woman to be given a primary diagnosis of depression, along with what doctors call a *comorbid* anxiety disorder.[4]

Finally, there is another condition listed in the DSM-IV-TR that is often considered as a diagnosis in the perinatal period. It's an *adjustment disorder*: a time-limited, but significant, emotional response to a stressful event; in this case, of course, that event primarily being the conception or birth of a child.[3]

Diagnostic criteria for adjustment disorder adapted from *Diagnostic and Statistical Manual of Mental Disorders, 4th edition — Text Revision* (DSM-IV-TR)[2]

Development of emotional or behavioural symptoms in response to a stressful event or situation, occurring within three months of the onset of the stressor.

Symptoms are clinically significant as evidenced by:
• significant impairment in social or occupational functioning
• marked distress in excess of what would be expected in response to the stressor.

Disorder does not meet the diagnostic criteria for another specific disorder (eg major depressive disorder).

Symptoms do not represent bereavement (ie not a grief reaction).

Symptoms do not persist for more than six months once the stressful event or situation has ended.

Subtypes include: with depressed mood, with anxiety, with mixed anxiety and depressed mood.

Whilst getting an accurate diagnosis is important, it's not necessary to get too hung up on the label. Ultimately, having a precise name for your condition matters less than the fact you are getting the right help and treatment for it.

SEEING YOUR DOCTOR

I remember one day… [the maternal and child health nurse] asked me to complete the Edinburgh Postnatal Depression questionnaire. She told me that my score indicated that I probably had postnatal depression and to see my GP. I saw my GP who is very good… she agreed that I was definitely suffering postnatal depression.

Once I finally got to the GP she was fantastic, she diagnosed postnatal depression immediately and put me on medication. I was glad that someone finally recognised that what I was going through wasn't normal and that they could help.

Your GP is usually your first port of call for diagnosis, assessment and treatment. When you are making a first appointment with your GP, it's a good idea to request a double appointment, if possible, as you'll need quite a bit of time to get to the bottom of things. In fact, your doctor may need to see you on a few occasions before they're prepared to make a definite diagnosis. It's a good idea to take some notes with you, with the questions you'd like to ask, and ideally a companion for support.

If your symptoms are not severe and your personal circumstances reasonably uncomplicated, you and your GP may be able to manage your treatment together, without the need for any specialist involvement. Typically, your GP would draw up a mental health care plan, covering possible options such as lifestyle changes, medication, referral to a psychologist (see page 100) for further assessment and treatment, or occasionally, 'watchful waiting' (close observation, to make sure things get better rather than worse) and support.

Your doctor should also organise some blood tests to rule out other conditions that could potentially be contributing to your mood; thyroid function testing is particularly important, along with iron, vitamin B12 and folate levels.

If you already have an established and harmonious relationship with your family GP, that's wonderful. However, not all women are so fortunate, at least in the first instance. In fact, if this is your first baby you may have hardly stuck your head in a doctor's surgery for years prior to your pregnancy, except perhaps to get a prescription for the occasional cold or flu.

This is a different situation. Your GP will need to arrange to see you regularly to monitor you, provide support and ongoing treatment. They will become an important person in your life, at least in the short term, and the relationship needs to be a healthy, supportive one.

If you don't feel comfortable with your current GP — if you feel they are too busy, not sufficiently empathetic or not knowledgeable enough about treatment options — you have the right to change. PANDA has a directory of GPs who have a special interest in perinatal anxiety and depression (see page 278).

If there are no GPs in your area with a special interest in perinatal mental health, that's ok too. Ultimately, the attitude of your GP is more crucial than whether they possess specialist knowledge. If they are prepared to give you time and really listen to your story, and make an effort to find people with the expertise they personally lack, these are more important qualities.

Word of mouth is very important when looking for a GP. If you don't feel up to asking around yourself, please get your friends and family to inquire on your behalf.

Insider's tip

Good GPs are highly sought after and, especially if you live in the country, it can sometimes be hard to get in to see them. If the doctor's receptionist says you will need to wait several weeks for an appointment, please get the person calling to inform the receptionist that you may be 'depressed', or whatever term you are comfortable with (although we'd recommend you don't just say you are having trouble 'coping' as almost all new mothers might rightly claim this) and need to see, or at least talk to, a doctor soon. If you prefer, you can ask your maternal and child health nurse to contact the GP on your behalf.

Doctors usually leave some space in their schedule to see urgent cases.

It's important not to abuse the goodwill of doctors by claiming a medical problem is urgent when it isn't, but an untreated perinatal mood disorder is a condition which you can rightly claim requires prompt attention.

If your case is more complicated and your symptoms are more severe your GP may refer you on to a specialist, such as a psychiatrist, for further assessment. Occasionally, a woman may need to be referred immediately from screening or hospital to a psychiatrist for diagnosis and treatment, especially if there are concerns about self-harm or a serious illness, such as puerperal psychosis, is suspected.

Although neither your obstetrician nor paediatrician (whom you may see with your new baby for a six-week check) is trained in the diagnosis and treatment of perinatal mental health disorders, they can assist you in finding help if you let them know that you need it.

A message to doctors

As we mentioned, not all doctors are as knowledgeable with regard to perinatal anxiety and depression as we'd hope. Here is a heartfelt plea from one woman who found this out the hard way:

Perinatal mood disorders are difficult to diagnose. What new mother doesn't feel overwhelmed, exhausted, and tearful at some point? But that is where you are so important. You will often be the first place that a woman will turn. And most women are not going to turn up already self-diagnosed. The inner lives of new mothers can be very opaque. Often, as you all know, there is another issue. The difficulty for you is to work out if there is a real problem. That takes time and you don't always have the time. I guess the trick is to be

> *mindful of the lives of the new parents you see and sensitive to what might pass between you in conversation, and to have some good referral options.*

THE DIAGNOSTIC ASSESSMENT

I will take a thorough history with particular reference to her own mental health issues in the past and look at all that is going on in her life that may make her at risk. I will also balance this with any protective factors eg supportive relationships, ability to communicate feelings etc... I conduct a Mental Status examination and possibly use some questionnaires on depression, anxiety and stress. Sometimes it is that a woman is on the fence and I may ask her to return in a few weeks time to see me. (health professional)

Ongoing assessment/monitoring and treatment are paramount following a provisional diagnosis. A definitive diagnosis can take more than one session. (health professional)

The health professional — commonly a doctor, psychologist or social worker — conducting the assessment should ask you a range of questions related to these topics:

- **Your current life situation**: How much support are you receiving from your partner; family; and friends? Do you have other children at home? Do you have any financial worries? How are you feeling about being pregnant or a mum? If your baby has been born: How was the birth? How is breastfeeding going?

- **Your symptoms and their severity**: Are you feeling moodier than usual? Do you feel like yourself? Can you sleep at night? If not, is it the baby keeping you awake or your own thoughts? How long have you felt this way? Do you feel depressed/

anxious only some of the time or almost all of the time? Have you had any unusual or scary thoughts? *Have you had any thoughts of suicide; self-harm; or hurting the baby?*

- **Your past history and family history:** Have you been treated for anxiety or depression in the past? Has someone in your family ever suffered from depression or anxiety, had a 'nervous breakdown' or other mental health problems?

- **Any other health problems, including eating disorders, drug and alcohol use or other chronic health issues:** How often do you drink alcohol? Are you taking any prescribed or alternative medicines? Does the baby have any health problems?

The health professional may ask you to complete some questionnaires to check on your mood at that moment in time; commonly they would use the Edinburgh Postnatal Depression Scale, but possibly also other validated questionnaires that assess anxiety and depression levels.

However, as the saying goes, 90% of communication is non-verbal. An experienced observer will be looking for non-verbal cues to assess your mood: things like your physical appearance (eg dull eyes, fixed smile or just looking generally 'flat') and *the manner* in which you say things as much as the words you say.

In depression, symptoms include:
- *tearfulness*
- *negative self talk*
- *irritability.*

In anxiety, symptoms are things like:
- *not wanting to be left alone with the baby*
- *nervous and pressured speech. (health professional)*

There also might be behavioural cues in a mother's relationship with her baby. Is she responsive? Sensitive? (health professional)

Severe depression goes along with 'psychomotor retardation'. The patient is... very slowed down, hardly moving, not eating, suffering severe sleep problems. Her thoughts may be racing but the outsider will not see this. These women look depressed as they no longer care for themselves and are in no fit state to put on a brave face. This is very serious and must be treated promptly. (health professional)

If you'd like more information, the Black Dog Institute has produced a fact sheet called, *What to expect from a mental health consultation?* which is available to download at the Black Dog website.

How you can help in your own diagnostic assessment

One thing to keep in mind as a clinician is the possibility that a woman won't want to tell you about her experience... some women will still feel ashamed, guilty or be concerned about the consequences of disclosing negative feelings or experiences. Equally, these worries and concerns are fed directly by the depression or anxiety. Women are very capable of deciding whether or not to disclose these issues, and they are smart. (health professional)

I didn't resist being diagnosed; I think it was somewhat of a relief. I was just concerned that my breastfeeding obsession had caused it. After the diagnosis and agreement on the course of treatment, I started to wonder if it was the other way around — the proverbial 'chicken and egg' conundrum.

I think most woman know when they are not coping as well as they would like to be. Some, initially, would prefer to hang this on tiredness/hormonal shifts. However, once given the opportunity to discuss their feelings... with a supportive person, they are usually open to the idea.(health professional)

I didn't want people to think I was crazy so I wasn't always honest with people. In fact I was very good at faking being well.

Being given a diagnosis is a relief for some women. They like having a name to latch on to, a medical explanation for feeling so lousy. Many others, however, may resist a diagnosis. They may be reluctant to disclose emotional problems to a health professional or feel the social stigma of having a mental health disorder. Some women may be so keen to preserve an image of themselves as competent mothers that they will try initially to mask or minimise symptoms.

The writer, Allison Pearson, author of the best-selling women's novel, *I Don't Know How She Does It*, recently wrote about 'cheating' in a depression questionnaire for these very reasons:

My pen hesitated. I wanted to be sure I circled the right answer. Despite the fact I'd finally felt rotten enough to seek professional help, pride dictated that I still came across as the best kind of girl to be... So I chose the most upbeat answers I could find.[5]

We discussed the Edinburgh Postnatal Depression Scale in the previous chapter, and how it's relatively easy to work out the answers you are required to give, to demonstrate that you are *not* depressed (even if you really are). We also explained how this helps no-one in the long run. The same warning applies here. This is not the place for putting on a brave face. If you take nothing else away from this chapter please remember this.

As Allison Pearson found out, when the psychiatrist she'd consulted subsequently diagnosed her with depression anyway, experienced professionals will most likely see through your attempts to cover up. As we said, the astute observer and interviewer will pick up the telltale clues.

The things I look out for in new mothers are:
- *racing thoughts*

- *'hyper' functioning*
- *worrying about every little thing*
- *worries about the baby's health*
- *feeling 'time pressure'*
- *clinging obsessively to routine, having to fit around babies' feed/sleep schedule*
- *worrying about what other people think of their parenting*
- *needing to appear perfect and on top of everything. (health professional)*

The Edinburgh Postnatal Depression Scale is a good starting point but... should be used within the context of clinical judgement. Any incongruent scores that do not match my clinical assessment or overly low scores are important alerts for me. (health professional)

So that your consultation is a success it's best you talk as openly as possible about how difficult things are for you. The person you'll be speaking to is a professional who has heard it all before. They will certainly not judge you — they only wish to help — and are bound by laws of confidentiality; anything you say will remain in the consulting room.

Another thing to be mindful of is that you will probably be feeling extremely sensitive at this time; it's actually a symptom of depression, although all pregnant women and new mothers tend to feel sensitive from time to time. If the health professional says anything you regard as hurtful or offensive, please let them know, so they can clarify what they mean. Otherwise this may poison a potentially good relationship.

Finally, it's good idea to take someone else along with you for the assessment, at least for the first appointment. They may remember things you've forgotten and you'll be less likely to gloss over your troubles with the health professional if you have a loved one in the room. In the process, your companion may learn more about perinatal anxiety and depression and this can only help in your journey to recovery.

6
TREATMENT AND RECOVERY — TALKING THERAPIES

The path of care depends on severity, experience and the woman's own preference. (health professional)

Treatment depends on the presenting problem. Some people just need some practical strategies in place, some need drugs and counselling, some just need counselling. (health professional)

I am very optimistic and do find women respond well to therapy with postnatal depression. However, I find if their family of origin is very dysfunctional then therapy can go for longer. (health professional)

If you've been diagnosed with perinatal anxiety and depression, the sooner you seek treatment and start on that road to recovery the better. However, the ideal therapy will be different from one person to the next, and will depend on a variety of factors including: the severity of your symptoms, personal preferences and unfortunately, for some, access to treatments. The sad reality is that if you are living in a major capital city the range of services available to you will be much greater than if you are living in a rural or remote area. Similarly, if English isn't your first language you may find it harder to access the full range of therapies available for perinatal mood disorders.

Cost can also prove a barrier, but fortunately there is now government support, such as the Better Access to Mental Health Care scheme (see page 285) and ATAPS (Access to Allied Psychological Services) to help defray some of the cost of counselling and psychological services.

Finally, there is the not so small matter of your illness, and for some this may prove the biggest hurdle of all to overcome. If you're feeling really down it can be a struggle just to get to the GP, let alone negotiate the whole therapy roundabout. If you have a family member or friend who can support you through this process, please don't feel bad about asking them for help. We talk more about getting support in Chapter 12.

TREATMENT OPTIONS

We can broadly break down treatments into a few available options:

- **Information and support**

- **Counselling and psychological treatments**, including cognitive behaviour therapy (CBT), interpersonal psychotherapy and psychodynamic therapy

- **Medications**, most commonly, use of antidepressants

- **Alternative therapies**, such as acupuncture, supplements and herbal medicines

The pros and cons of medications and alternative therapies are discussed in Chapter 7, but for the moment we will concentrate on the first two in the list above, in particular counselling and psychological treatments, which collectively are commonly referred to as the 'talking therapies'.

Your symptoms, your management plan[1]

- Generally speaking, if your symptoms are assessed as mild you should be able to develop a management plan with your GP, enlisting outside support, counselling and perhaps some psychological help to get you back on your feet.

- However, if your symptoms are moderate to severe, and really impacting on your ability to function at home, you may require medication (see Chapter 7), in combination with psychological therapy and counselling, to put you on the road to recovery.

- If your depression and/or anxiety is severe and distressing and/or doesn't respond to the usual treatments, you may be referred to a psychiatrist or a hospital-based mental health service for specialist management.

- For women with severe and acute symptoms — which may or may not indicate another diagnosis, such as bipolar disorder or puerperal psychosis (see page 39) — or intrusive thoughts of self-harm, or harm to others, admission to hospital for specialised support may be the best option. Mother-baby units allow new mothers to get treatment in a supportive and parent-friendly environment.

INFORMATION

We need more education around postnatal depression and breaking the stigma of asking for help and admitting things are hard. And less 'right and wrong' information [about child rearing]. Everyone is entitled to parent in their own way and it's not the end of the world if breastfeeding doesn't work or a woman doesn't want to follow a strict routine. (health professional)

Sometimes emotional problems may simply be triggered by lack of information or incorrect beliefs about a situation: not knowing or being told the wrong things.

There are so many conflicting sources of information about parenting that it's often difficult to know whom to believe. Every day it seems that there is a new parenting book published, some advocating a disciplinary 'controlled crying' approach, others espousing a caring, sharing 'co-sleeping' philosophy. Each will have its enthusiastic supporters and an equal number of passionate detractors. When this is combined with well-meaning but sometimes inaccurate advice from relatives, friends and occasionally even complete strangers, you can end up feeling very confused.

Similarly the internet, for all its benefits, is largely uncensored. This means that anyone can set up a website and express their views, no matter how extreme. If you are feeling emotionally vulnerable, reading this sort of unvetted pregnancy and parenting information can prove very distressing.

That's why it's important to seek out correct and reliable information. Reputable information sources may include: midwives, obstetricians, paediatricians, GPs, midwives, and child and family health nurses. These professionals all have a role in providing information for new and prospective parents about pregnancy and typical infant development. They will hopefully also be able to set you straight on any misinformation you read or hear.

A directory of reputable information sources is provided in our Resources Guide.

A word of warning, however; we can't guarantee that all health professionals will be equally helpful. If you detect a judgemental attitude from anyone you consult, or receive advice that conflicts with what you've heard elsewhere, it's ok to move on and seek out more open-minded professionals for your information. Parenting is an inexact science and there is no single way to do it well.

Pregnancy, Birth and Baby Helpline
1800 882 436

Started in 2010, this is a Federal Government initiative which offers free telephone support to families and carers, from the first signs of pregnancy through to baby's first birthday. Information and referrals can be provided on a huge number of topics, including conception, all aspects of pregnancy care, birthing, and the care of babies and their parents. The line is open 24 hours a day, seven days a week.

If you are looking for parenting information on the internet, it's a good idea to stick to websites that are supported by government or professional organisations.

The *Raising Children* website is a good Australian site:
http://raisingchildren.net.

Learning about parenting is one thing; we also need access to reliable information about perinatal mood disorders. If you've never been a mother before, how do you know whether the emotions you are feeling are just part of an adjustment process that all new mums go through, or if you really need help? Research suggests that many women don't seek help for their depression because they believe that 'feeling depressed' is an inevitable consequence of motherhood, or that their symptoms are not serious enough to warrant treatment.[2]

Never underestimate the value of good quality information. A recent Australian study found that providing targeted information in the form of a booklet — *beyondblue's Emotional Health During*

Pregnancy and Early Childhood — was as effective at preventing postnatal anxiety and depression in a group of 'at risk'* pregnant women as providing similar information in an antenatal cognitive behavioural therapy group.[3]

Of course, if you are reading this book, you are hopefully on the right track to getting the information you need.

TALKING THERAPIES — COUNSELLING AND PSYCHOLOGICAL TREATMENTS

Next time I will get counselling as soon as I get pregnant to keep the feelings under control and join a group and talk to people about it.

Treatment is given to each person as a person. I respect their ability to parent and get through this difficulty and I give them lots of suggestions to work through. It's important not to overtake and become authoritarian in approach. (health professional)

It was incredibly cathartic and at the end of my first session I took a breath and felt like a huge weight had been lifted. The counsellor's feedback to me was 'you've suffered multiple losses the past few years' — she was right.

For those experiencing mild anxiety and depression some counselling and emotional support may be all that's needed to get through this difficult period. Finding an empathetic listener who can offer an explanation for your symptoms, a little bit of hope and a path forward, is therapeutic in itself.

There are many different counselling approaches.

*Either demonstrating mild to moderate symptoms, or considered at risk because of social factors and/or a past history of depression and anxiety.

In *supportive counselling* the counsellor's role is not to tell you what to do, but to simply be a good listener and provide emotional support, encouraging you to find your own solutions to your problems. Many therapists, however, will combine counselling with psychological treatments, such as cognitive behaviour therapy and interpersonal therapy (see below).

Counselling can focus on you alone or on your key relationships; for example couples' counselling or family therapy. It can take place in an individual or group setting, face-to-face or via the telephone or internet.

You may not know yet which is the most suitable counselling model for you. For many women, regular individual counselling consultations will prove most helpful, but others (after an initial individual assessment) may prefer the camaraderie of a group.

Psychological treatments

I see patients for as many sessions as required. I often find women with postnatal depression respond well to therapy and within four to five sessions are starting to feel much better. (health professional)

She helped me with cognitive behaviour therapy... to regain control of my thoughts and feelings and to shift them from positive to negative.

Psychological treatments are commonly recommended for perinatal anxiety and depression. They can be effective when used alone for the management of mild to moderate symptoms, but are often used in combination with medication for more severe and treatment-resistant cases.

The three best-studied of these psychological treatments are described below. After reading these descriptions it's possible that one psychological therapy may look more appealing to you. You can ask around for a psychologist who specialises in a particular therapy, although many therapists will be skilled in more than one method and ideally will tailor the therapy around your individual needs.

When it comes to the crunch it's more important you find someone who is sympathetic to the particular challenges surrounding pregnancy and new parenthood, than the best known 'guru' of a particular therapy.

Counselling versus psychological treatments

Whilst we've made a distinction between counselling and psychological treatments in this book, once you're in the care of a skilled therapist the difference may not be obvious.

Psychological treatments are based on a scientifically-validated approach and the therapist will provide you with active strategies to follow. This distinguishes them from counselling, which mainly involves listening and reflecting. However, many health professionals, including some professional counsellors, will employ psychological strategies as part of a therapy program. The line between counselling and psychological treatments can therefore seem hazy.

Whatever talking therapy road you take the aim should be to examine your beliefs about yourself and motherhood, look for possible triggers — past and present — for your symptoms, and develop a plan to cope with the day-to-day challenges of living with perinatal anxiety and depression. At the end of this process you will hopefully find yourself stronger and more resilient than you have ever been.

Cognitive behaviour therapy

Cognitive behaviour therapy (CBT) is the best-studied psychological treatment for depression in general and perinatal depression in particular.[4] It is also effective at managing anxiety disorders, including posttraumatic stress disorder.[5]

CBT aims to help you identify negative thinking patterns,

evaluate them and change them for more realistic ones. If our thoughts are changed for the better, the theory goes, our mood and feelings should follow. A short course of CBT (anywhere from 6–12 sessions) can prove effective for many people.

These days there are many 'offshoots' from CBT; some you may encounter include Acceptance and Commitment Therapy (ACT), Mindfulness Based Cognitive Therapy (MBCT), and Dialectical Behavioural Therapy (DBT). These incorporate a form of Buddhist meditation called 'mindfulness' which teaches people to be completely in touch with the present moment, and notice their thoughts, feelings and experiences without trying to change them. Whilst previously these therapies might have been described as 'alternative' in some circles, they do appear to show promise in the treatment and prevention of depression.

Help on the internet

MoodGYM — *CBT online* Developed by the Centre for Mental Health Research at the Australian National University (ANU), MoodGYM is an evidence-based, interactive web-based program designed to prevent depression. It teaches the principles of cognitive behaviour therapy (CBT) as well as relaxation and meditation techniques.
http://moodgym.anu.edu.au/welcome

Based at St Vincent's Hospital in Sydney, **CRUfAD** is another excellent online resource. It contains a self-help section on anxiety and depression. To access the CRUfAD Clinic, their online CBT program, you require a referral from your GP.
www.crufad.org/

Another initiative of the Centre for Mental Health Research at the ANU, *e-couch* provides evidence-based information about depression and anxiety, and teaches strategies to help prevent problems.
http://ecouch.anu.edu.au/welcome

Interpersonal psychotherapy

Interpersonal psychotherapy (IPT) assumes that a stressful event, such as pregnancy and childbirth, when combined with insufficient social support, can make us vulnerable to depression and that interpersonal difficulties can, to a greater or lesser extent, contribute to this.

The aim of IPT is to help us understand events in interpersonal terms and explore alternative ways of handling situations. Therapy initially focuses on interpersonal conflict and role changes, aiming to improve communication or readjust expectations. Secondly, IPT teaches people how to enlist the support of others to help them through the immediate crisis and build resilience for the future.

Psychodynamic psychotherapy

Psychodynamic psychotherapy is a derivative of psychoanalysis, originally developed by Sigmund Freud. It focuses on *unconscious* thoughts and feelings (that is, those of which we are unaware) and how these manifest in our present-day behaviour. The goals of therapy are to increase a patient's self-awareness, and to help them interpret the influence of past conflicts and childhood experiences on their current behaviour, with the objective of working through these.

Finding the right therapist

Everyone needs a confidant. Women who are socially isolated are at higher risk of perinatal mood disorders. Depressed mothers commonly cite 'lack of support' and 'feeling isolated' as reasons behind their low mood.[6]

Finding the right person to talk to is extremely important. The relationship between you and your chosen therapist may play a big role in how quickly you progress with your therapy.

Following is a list of professionals who may be able to help.

GPs

Some GPs have undergone specialist training in mental health and may offer counselling and psychological treatments themselves.

There are facilities under the Medicare Better Access to Mental Health Care program for GPs to do this. See page 285 or visit the links below for more information.

---

beyondblue has an excellent fact sheet on getting help under Medicare; visit their website www.beyondblue.org.au or the Federal Government's www.health.gov.au for more information on the Better Access scheme.

However, it's more likely your GP will refer you to another professional, such as a psychologist, psychiatrist or professional counsellor for ongoing counselling.

Tackling stigmas

Research suggests that women with perinatal anxiety and depression may have trouble coming to terms with the fact they have a mental health disorder.

Mental health refers to an individual's emotional and psychological well-being. If your mental health is not good — specifically in this case if you're experiencing anxiety and depression — technically you do have a *mental health disorder*. However, we need to get over the idea that this is anything to be ashamed of. We hope we've made it clear that you are not to blame for this, any more than you would be to blame for developing a debilitating physical ailment.

Similarly, seeking counselling or psychological treatment for your anxiety and depression should not be seen as a sign of 'failure', but as a first step towards recovery. The authors of this book are happy to 'out' themselves as former or current therapy users and swear by its benefits.

Remember that any guilt or shame you may be feeling about your diagnosis is in all likelihood a cleverly disguised symptom of the depression itself.

Psychologists

As a psychologist the main help I provide is psychological therapy, monitoring medications with doctors and tapping women into supportive organisations and people who will help their recovery. (health professional)

A psychologist is a health care professional who has university qualifications and postgraduate training in human thinking and behaviour. Clinical psychologists are psychologists who have undergone additional specialist training and have a doctorate or masters degree in psychology. Some clinical psychologists have chosen to specialise in perinatal mental health — we list some ways you can find them below.

Psychologists (including clinical psychologists) are not medically trained and cannot prescribe medication; instead they use counselling and scientifically-supported psychological treatments to help change behaviour and emotions.

In Australia, all psychologists are required to register with their state or territory registration board. They may work in hospitals, mental health units, community health or private practice (see Resources Guide).

If you are planning to consult a private psychologist and wish to claim Medicare rebates for these consultations you will need to obtain a referral from your GP (who will prepare a mental health care plan) or psychiatrist. You can claim for up to 12 individual or group services a year, although your referring doctor is required to assess your progress after six sessions. For more information see page 285.

Alternatively — if you have the right 'extras' cover — you may be able to claim a refund for psychological services from your private health insurance. However, this is an either/or situation; you cannot claim from Medicare and your private health insurer for the same consultation.

The Australian Psychological Society website contains lots of useful information, including a search facility which allows you to locate psychologists who have an interest in perinatal mental health disorders in your local area. **www.psychology.org.au/**

The *beyondblue* and PANDA websites also provide online search facilities to help you locate private psychologists in your region.

Psychiatrists

Psychiatrists are doctors with a medical degree who specialise in the diagnosis and treatment of mental health disorders, including mood and anxiety disorders. They often employ counselling and psychological therapies in combination with medication, and commonly work in collaboration with psychologists and other mental health professionals.

Psychiatrists work in hospitals, community mental health services, universities and/or in private practice. You can be referred to a psychiatrist by your GP or, on occasions, another doctor, such as your obstetrician.

Medicare rebates are available for private psychiatrist consultations, although in many cases you will be required to make a 'gap' payment.

Counsellors

Professional counsellors have formal qualifications in counselling. Often this is combined with training in *psychotherapy* (sometimes described as a more 'in-depth' form of counselling). Other counsellors may come from health backgrounds such as nursing or social work. *Counselling psychologists* are psychologists who have training in both counselling and psychology.

However, counsellors are not required to be professionally registered with the government, so technically anyone can call themselves a 'counsellor'.

Therefore, if you are consulting a counsellor privately, it would be a good idea to check their qualifications and training, and whether they are accredited by a professional body such as the Psychotherapy and Counselling Federation of Australia Inc (PAFCA) or the Australian Counselling Association (ACA).

Unless a counsellor is registered by Medicare (eg they are a counselling psychologist, a mental health social worker or occupational therapist — see below), you cannot claim a rebate for counselling consultations. If you have private health insurance 'extras' cover you may be able to claim for some counselling services, but it would be wise to check with your fund beforehand.

Free or low cost counselling is available through community health centres, charities and religious organisations (see Resources Guide).

When it comes to perinatal anxiety and depression, some of the most effective counsellors are often the 'survivors' — women who've been through it themselves and emerged the other side. **PANDA** offers a free telephone helpline **1300 726 306** that is staffed by professional counsellors and trained volunteers, most of whom have experienced perinatal mood disorders first-hand. It operates Monday to Friday 9am–7pm. Whilst it is not designed to be a substitute for individual counselling, the helpline can provide information, support and referral to other service providers.

For couple or family counselling, **Relationships Australia** is a useful first port of call. Their counselling fees are on a sliding-scale, adjusted according to household income. Call **1300 364 277** or visit **www.relationships.com.au.**

Occupational therapists and social workers

Most occupational therapists and social workers work in public health and welfare system. However, a small number work in private practice and can offer similar counselling services to psychologists. If your GP prepares a mental health care plan and refers you to an accredited Mental Health Occupational Therapist or Mental

Health Social Worker, the cost of consultations should be fully or partially covered by Medicare.

To locate an accredited Mental Health Social Worker, see the Australian Association of Social Workers website: **www.aasw.asn.au.**

For accredited Mental Health Occupational Therapists visit Occupational Therapy Australia: **www.ausot.com.au.**

Some women may be eligible to receive psychological treatment through **Access to Allied Psychological Services** (ATAPS), another Federal Government-funded program. Health professionals who may be able to provide psychological services through ATAPS include psychologists, social workers, mental health nurses, occupational therapists and Aboriginal and Torres Strait Islander health workers with specific mental health qualifications.

See page 285 for more information about ATAPS.

AN IMPORTANT RELATIONSHIP

I eventually saw a psychologist for several sessions who was lovely and very helpful.

I told the last therapist that I saw about the anxiety I've been feeling about my daughter. Her response: 'Look, as long as your daughter has food in her belly and a roof over her head, there's nothing to worry about. Stop worrying.' Hence, I stopped seeing her. I'm sure she meant well, but I found myself feeling worse after seeing her than before.

In response to my outburst of uncontrollable crying when discussing my 'failure at breastfeeding', she said 'you're traumatised' — she was right. She was warm. She did not focus on postnatal depression; she helped me to explore every aspect of my life, including significant points in my history, flexibly and openly.

Qualities you should be looking for in a counsellor/therapist*
include:

- appropriate professional qualifications and training
- some specialist knowledge of perinatal anxiety and depression
- a reputation for professionalism (word-of-mouth may help here)
- accessibility — if possible, it's best to find a therapist who practises close by, although the telephone and internet can now be used to overcome geographical barriers.

However, these factors are only part of the equation. Therapists are people too, and therefore will differ in their personality, values and beliefs. The personal attributes of the therapist may be as, or even more, important than any university degrees and doctorates hanging on their walls.

It's really important you connect with your therapist. Women generally find they respond more quickly if they feel their therapist is understanding and empathetic and 'gets' where they're coming from. Ask yourself: Do they seem compassionate; open-minded; willing to listen and not judge? Can they provide me a path forward? Does talking to them make me feel better or worse?

Even if you do your research thoroughly, it's possible you may not find the right person first time around. It's worth remembering that depression can make you feel oversensitive — and thus occasionally lead you to take offence at a well-intentioned comment — but if your therapist seems consistently critical, old-fashioned in their beliefs about perinatal mood disorders, or simply not very interested, then they may not be the right person for you.

If you find you still aren't clicking with your chosen therapist after a suitable trial (three sessions is about appropriate) it would be best to look for someone else. It is not uncommon for women to 'shop around' for a while before finding a professional they really connect with.

---

* for ease of discussion we will use the general term 'therapist', to denote any psychologist, psychotherapist, counsellor, social worker or doctor you consult.

Finally, like any worthwhile relationship, therapy requires a commitment. *Once you've found the right person* please try your best to stick to the therapy timetable they recommend. Don't be tempted to call a stop after a couple of sessions even if you do believe you're feeling 'better'. Your road to recovery will not be a simple path; you will have good days and bad days along the way. It's generally recommended that you continue seeing your therapist for some time after the worst of your symptoms have resolved — although possibly at less frequent intervals — to reduce the chance of relapse.

PRACTICAL AND SOCIAL SUPPORT

The other part of my treatment was the support that my mum gave me... Her patience in giving me the support when I needed it, as well as the confidence to start looking after my own baby, are the single most important things that kept me out of hospital. She never judged me and most importantly, she never put any pressure on me to do things that I was not comfortable with. She obviously had my dad (perinatal psychiatrist) guiding her on a daily basis to make sure that I reached my full recovery when I was ready and able.

Depression and anxiety are very isolating. For those fortunate to have a sympathetic partner, family, and friends, harnessing their help can make a big difference. The young woman quoted above was clearly blessed to have such a supportive mum (and dad).

However, we acknowledge that even the apparently 'simple' act of asking for help may prove daunting right now. When you're feeling depressed and anxious, motivation is usually one of the first casualties. Tasks that once were easy may suddenly seem *very, very* hard. Thus, one of the first issues your therapist may have to work with you to address is self-care and asking for help.

Also, not all of us will be fortunate enough — like the young lady above — to have a father who is a psychiatrist. Nonetheless, your family and friends will be more able to provide the emotional and practical support you need if they can understand what you're going through. We recommend that you point them towards some of the excellent resources available for the families and friends of people experiencing depression — the websites of PANDA, the Black Dog Institute and *beyondblue* are good places to start.

Right now is no time to be a martyr. If you are lucky enough to be able to afford outside domestic help, please get some. Otherwise you could ask your family and friends for help with housework and cooking. You may be pleasantly surprised at their response. If you find you have trouble asking for assistance, you could simply refer them to Chapter 12 of this book.

Alternatively, grandparents and extended family members can care for baby while you catch up on your sleep, exercise, or just take time out to pursue a hobby or passion. These are not frivolous activities — they all are all things we know will help in your recovery.

Even if your family does not live nearby, please try to avoid isolating yourself too much. Stay in touch with loved ones as much as possible, even if it's only by phone, email or Skype. We also suggest you look around your local community for the help you need. In particular, try to meet other families with similar aged children. Places to look for friendship and support include: local councils, libraries, community health centres, playgroups, church and school communities, charities and other voluntary groups.

We are not saying any of this will be simple. In the short term it may seem easier to do nothing, but the research tells us it certainly won't prove easier in the long run. One of the keys to tackling depression, in particular, is self-care and that means getting help and getting out, to do the things you enjoy.

Of course, sometimes more formal support is required.

OTHER FORMS OF SUPPORT

Perinatal anxiety and depression support groups

As hard as it was to go and sit in with a group and talk about stuff, it was also comforting to be in a room and know that there were other people as messed up as I was!

I just did talking therapy — just what I needed, being in a group with others I could relate to and not being judged.

Run by community-based organisations, hospital perinatal mental health units, and, increasingly, early parenting centres (see following section) perinatal anxiety and depression support groups can be an enormous help.

Group therapy usually involves six to ten individuals and a facilitator, who guides discussion. The facilitator may be a professional therapist or, in some situations, a peer (a woman who has recovered from perinatal anxiety and depression). Discussions might revolve around symptoms of depression and anxiety, motherhood, parenting and relationship skills, and self-care strategies to aid in your recovery.

The advantage of support groups is that you will be mixing with other women in a similar situation, who can offer their own perspectives, understanding and support in a respectful environment. Partners can also receive support, through evening sessions and social activities.

> Perinatal depression support groups run in all states and territories in Australia. Check the Resources Guide for more information.

That said, groups do not always suit everyone. Attendance is required at a particular time and place and naturally this will be more convenient for some than others. Transport, time constraints, and — particularly for mothers with more than one child — lack of child care, can all make group sessions problematical.

Some women may also be uncomfortable revealing personal feelings, even to a sympathetic group. If this description fits you, no-one will oblige you to attend group sessions; talk to your therapist beforehand about your concerns.

Supported playgroups for women experiencing postnatal depression are one answer to the thorny problem of childcare; these run in much the same way as a normal playgroup, except that sessions are facilitated by a trained support worker.

However, supported playgroups are a more appropriate forum for women who have already finished a course with a postnatal depression support group and, at the time of writing, are few and far between. Once again, check the Resources Guide for listings.

Not all groups may be supportive

Often women put other women down when they are in a vulnerable position themselves, to build up their own sense of self-worth. This can happen in very subtle ways in mothers' groups, particularly with first-time mums.

We need to be clear here. The groups we are referring to above are those *specifically for women are experiencing symptoms of perinatal anxiety and/or depression.* These are different to the *new mother's groups* that child and family health nurses often recommend you join after your baby is born.

In the right circumstances new mothers' groups can be both educational and an excellent way to make new friends. However, if you're depressed and anxious, mixing with mothers who appear to be content and coping — bearing in mind that some of them may not be coping nearly as well as they say — can be a challenge.

Ask yourself: Does attending this group make me feel better or worse about myself? If it's the latter, it may be best to avoid your new mother's group until you are feeling healthier. You could maybe ask your nurse to refer you to a different group, or try to seek companionship in other ways.

Early parenting centres

Early parenting centres offer practical support to families struggling with the challenges of early parenthood. They can provide guidance and support on a range of issues, such as: feeding (breastfeeding, bottle feeding and introducing solids), sleep and settling routines, child development, adjustment to parenthood and relationships.

Early parenting centres may offer any of the following services:

- on-the-spot advice (many centres offer their own telephone helpline)
- referral to parent education sessions
- an outreach service
- a day-stay program
- a residential program.

For some services, such as the day-stay and residential programs, you will need a referral from a child and family health nurse or doctor.

Some early parenting centres are now offering counselling, postnatal depression support groups and other services specifically directed towards the needs of women experiencing perinatal anxiety and depression.

Most services offered by government-funded parenting centres are free of charge. Their residential programs are either covered by Medicare or private insurance (if you have cover), although parents may be required to pay a small accommodation and meals charge per day. Residential programs operated by private centres may be claimable on private health insurance.

Check the Resources Guide for early parenting centres in your state.

Hospitalisation

Even though I was a voluntary patient in the private clinic I was still there a little reluctantly. I did admit to myself that I was unable to cope... and if that meant being in a hospital for a few weeks to get medication sorted and get back on track, then so be it... There were twice daily group counselling sessions and daily sessions with the psychiatrist that made all the difference... It was a difficult time being away from the family but completely necessary.

The majority of women with perinatal anxiety and depression can remain at home and be successfully treated in the local community. On occasion, however, a woman's symptoms may be severe enough to warrant admission to hospital.

A mother and baby unit is a specialised unit within a public or private hospital, in which mothers and their babies room together. In this environment the mother is able to receive the psychiatric treatment she requires, as well as the necessary support to be able to mother her baby. A multidisciplinary team — which may include psychiatrists, paediatricians, mental health nurses, psychologists, social workers and mothercraft nurses — is on hand to attend to both mother and baby's needs.

Treatment may include:
- medication
- individual therapy
- couple or family therapy
- group therapy
- meditation and relaxation
- exercise
- parenting skills
- fathers' sessions.

When the time comes for discharge, staff will work with the mother to link her up with community support services to make this transition as trouble-free as possible. PANDA have also produced a helpful fact sheet called *Coming home from a mother and baby unit: Coping in the first few weeks,* which you can download from the PANDA website.

Mother and baby units are listed in our Resources Guide. Unfortunately, at the time of writing there are not enough units in

Australia to meet the growing demand for services. Women living outside major metropolitan areas are particularly disadvantaged.

On very rare occasions a mother may be so ill (eg suffering from postnatal psychosis) that she is incapable of caring for her baby. In this situation she may be admitted to a general adult psychiatric facility, with her baby cared for by her partner, relatives or trusted friends.

Infant attachment therapy

One new treatment receiving increased attention is infant attachment therapy. Professor Bryanne Barnett, AM, is a Perinatal and Infant Psychiatry Consultant at Karitane Early Parenting Services NSW and St John of God Health Care, Blacktown, NSW. She kindly agreed to provide us with a brief overview of this fascinating therapeutic area.

We all know that the bond that forms between a child and his parents, * *especially the primary caregiver, ie the parent or other person who looked after the child consistently in the early months and years, is important as a foundation for relationships throughout their lives.*

Babies arrive in the world 'hard-wired' to attract and expect care giving from someone and they are dependent on caregivers for some years. Unlike many other higher primates, human babies cannot even stay close to their mother unless she picks them up and carries them — there is no fur to cling to. They cannot feed or maintain an appropriate temperature or be safe unless she makes this happen. If she is able to meet his physical and emotional needs sensitively, warmly and reliably, the baby will conclude that he is safe, lovable and a valuable person, who can expect effective help from others if he gets into difficulties interacting with and exploring the world. If something goes wrong and no-one else fills the gap adequately, the baby grows up thinking that he is not safe, not loved/lovable, and cannot or must not rely on others to help, thereby limiting his ability to build or maintain successful relationships into the future. (It is important here to remember that 'being' safe and 'feeling' safe are not necessarily the same thing.)

Thus the central premise of attachment theory is that parents who are sensitive and responsive to their infant's needs establish a sense of security.[7-10] The infant knows that the caregiver is dependable, which creates a secure base for the child to then explore their environment.

The strongest influence on the baby is the particular parent's own 'state of mind with respect to attachment' when interacting with and thinking about this baby (bearing in mind that a baby might feel safe and loved by one parent but not the other). Even where a mother has been significantly ill with depression, anxiety or other complications during or after pregnancy, or her baby has had to be in neonatal intensive care for a long period, she may be able to prevent this from adversely affecting her relationship with the infant, if her own attachment state of mind is secure. If, however, the mother's attachment pattern is insecure, the infant is also likely to be insecure unless we address this through interventions.

Many mother-infant interventions are based on attachment theory. These involve helping the parent/s to understand the child's signals and needs and how best to respond to these. The key aspect, however, is that the therapist offering the intervention must first make the parent feel safe, worthwhile and cared about before the parent will be in a position to consider his or her baby's feelings and needs. The parent must also feel sufficiently supported by the therapist and the therapy environment to be motivated to keep attending for many weeks.

Many different treatment programs can be successful provided these criteria are met (see Resources Guide for more information).

One such program is called: Watch, Wait and Wonder (WWW).[11] This program explicitly states that, although the infant's presence and involvement are required, the main feature is the relationship that develops between the therapist and the parent. The sessions may be held on an individual basis or in a group setting. First the baby and mother are on the floor playing; mother is asked to observe only, ie not to direct or initiate the interaction, but be attentive, and respond if baby initiates interaction. The therapist is also attentive and available but does not give directions during the interaction. In the second half of the session, the mother is invited to discuss her observations, thoughts and feelings. Thus both parent and baby are encouraged to feel safe and explore.

There are many similar programs, often making good use of filming to capture the mother-infant interaction (play, feeding, bathing) and allow discussion during a film playback session. An advantage of this is that the mother, although often nervous at first, is intrigued by the film and may be delighted to take home a copy of the session.

* To avoid confusion and unnecessary repetition in this section, the baby will be referred to as 'he' and the parent as 'she', despite the fact that babies are often girls and the main (or equal) caregiver may be the father.

That's the talking therapies and other non-drug supports in a nutshell. Remember that — as each of us follows an individual pathway to perinatal anxiety and depression — it's illogical to assume a single treatment method will be effective for all. You just need to find what works best for **you**.

7
TREATMENT AND RECOVERY — MEDICATIONS AND ALTERNATIVE THERAPIES

I think medication has definitely helped just to give me the 'lightness of mind' to be able to make the other changes I needed to make — mainly in my own outlook. It helped me to be able to work on controlling my anxiety, which in turn subdued all the other symptoms.

What helped the most? The combination of medication to get me through the worst of the anxiety, and also seeing the psychologist.

Probably the second most confronting issue you will have to deal with if you are diagnosed with a perinatal mood disorder — second only to admitting you have a problem in the first place — is the issue of taking medication to relieve your symptoms.

Of course, if your anxiety and depression is mild, medication may not be offered as part of your treatment. You may well be able to get through this with some counselling/psychological treatment and support. However, if you're one of the women for whom medication is recommended — and one report suggests about a third of women might fall into this category[1] — the purpose of this chapter is to help and inform you.

But what if you're pregnant or still breastfeeding? Being advised by a doctor to take medicine whilst you're pregnant or nursing goes against everything we've ever learnt. Don't the experts caution against taking anything except the occasional Panadol during pregnancy? In most circumstances this is correct advice, but we're not talking about most circumstances here. In the case of moderate to severe perinatal anxiety and depression — and more particularly if your diagnosis is bipolar disorder or puerperal psychosis — the risks of not treating are often greater than those of taking a medicine that has been studied for many years in pregnant and lactating women.

No-one is suggesting that medication is a panacea. Certainly no-one is recommending you take an antidepressant as a substitute for proper psychological help and support. However, many women have found that, as a result of taking an antidepressant, they have moved to 'a better place', allowing their chosen talking therapy to really have an impact.

What can happen if you don't take medication when it's recommended?

I was offered drugs but I refused — madness.

Untreated perinatal anxiety and depression can have a negative impact on the physical and mental wellbeing of not only a mother, but her baby, partner and other family members.

Researchers have found that untreated anxiety and depression during pregnancy may affect the developing infant, potentially resulting in:

- premature delivery
- 'difficult' temperaments
- increased levels of the stress hormone cortisol
- anxiety problems and behavioural and learning difficulties in childhood.[1-3]

Also, women who are depressed and anxious during pregnancy may not get proper antenatal care and may 'self-medicate' with alcohol, illegal drugs and cigarettes, all of which we know to be harmful to the baby.

For women with untreated postnatal anxiety and depression — apart from the immediate personal and relationship stresses it can cause — there is a risk they may develop chronic depression. Clearly we wish to avoid that.

If postnatal anxiety and depression symptoms are severe and remain untreated long-term, a mother's relationship with her infant may be affected, potentially leading to later emotional and behavioural problems for the child (see page 35).

The point we are trying to make is that there are potential benefits to your baby of fully treating your anxiety and depression. That's why a doctor may recommend you take medication, even if you are pregnant or breastfeeding. It's necessary to weigh up both the risks and benefits of treatment carefully.

MEDICATIONS — THE BASICS

It's not the intention of this book to give you all the information you need to know about medications for perinatal mood disorders, only to provide a brief summary of commonly used medicines as a starting point. The decision to take medicine should be a collaborative one, involving you, your partner, your GP, and, where appropriate, your obstetrician and/or psychiatrist.

ANTIDEPRESSANTS

At first I had to have the very old drugs as I was still breastfeeding and I did have awful side effects for the first few weeks… If I hadn't been so very desperate I don't know if I'd have stuck with them… Later I switched over to a very modern SSRI and it was much easier to deal with the few side effects.

Within about a week I was feeling a bit better. After a few weeks with the dose increased, I felt quite 'normal' again. It was amazing… Instead of having suicidal thoughts I was happy… My negative thoughts didn't disappear completely but I could think about the thoughts logically and realise that I didn't agree with them. My thoughts and even feelings were not right and I had the power to resist them rather than them overwhelming me.

The antidepressant did help a lot, almost immediately it seems. It helped me to sleep and took away most of my anxiety. The only downside was weight gain, which is why I went off it (under my GP's supervision) after only eight weeks or so (I was also getting better by this time).

The most frequently used medications in perinatal anxiety and depression are antidepressants and when we talk about medication use in this setting we are generally referring to this family of medicines.

Of the antidepressants, the most commonly prescribed are the *selective serotonin reuptake inhibitors,* or SSRIs, and, in turn, the most well known of the SSRIs is fluoxetine, better known by the tradename, Prozac®. If your main symptom is anxiety rather than depression, the SSRIs are still indicated, as they have potent anti-anxiety effects, too.

Table 1, below, provides a brief overview of the better-known antidepressants and their use in pregnancy and breastfeeding. Please note that, as there are many different brands of these antidepressants, we have only listed chemical (sometimes called 'generic') names, not trade names. Whenever you are prescribed any new medicine, it's recommended you ask your pharmacist for a Consumer Medicine Information leaflet for that particular brand.

Starting an antidepressant

I was prescribed an antidepressant with horrible start and withdrawal effects, so was also heavily medicated with sedatives to avoid additional anxiety when I started the meds... After I had my first 'good' day after about four weeks, I started to wean myself off the sedatives and rely on the antidepressants. My strongest memory is of the frustration I felt in having a good day which was then followed by a bad day. Fortunately I had an excellent psychiatrist who I saw one or two times a week for the first few months (until I stabilised) and she helped me understand the gradual journey towards being healthy and happy again... The medication and counselling were absolutely vital to my recovery.

Because I'd suffered clinical depression about 15 years ago, my GP was happy to prescribe the same medication I'd used then, as it had helped me with no side effects. However, I was sorely disappointed when the medication seemed not to have any effect in the same time frame as before. This time it took about six weeks for me to start feeling better and I had to push myself to make other changes at the same time.

If you are prescribed an antidepressant it is really important you understand that:
- it is not a miracle cure. If your doctor writes you a prescription and waves you off at the door without providing a detailed follow-up plan, *find yourself a new doctor!*
- your doctor should start you on a low dose and carefully

increase this until you feel a therapeutic effect (ie your mood improves) — the exact 'right' dose varies from one person to another. A 'start low, go slow' approach reduces the chance you will experience side effects.

- it may take several weeks for your antidepressant to take full effect, although hopefully you will notice some improvement in your mood within two to three weeks.

- if you are prescribed a SSRI you may even feel worse for a period (usually seven to ten days, but occasionally longer), with increased anxiety, agitation and negative thoughts. *Whilst these symptoms will usually settle down with time, it's essential you are closely monitored during this period. Seek help straight away if you begin to feel significantly worse, not better.*

- there may be a period of trial and error to find the right antidepressant for you. For reasons that are largely unknown, people often respond better to one antidepressant than another. If you have taken an antidepressant in the past — and it proved effective — your doctor may try that one as first-choice. Of course, if you are pregnant or breastfeeding your doctor will have to take into consideration these factors as well.

- you should not stop an antidepressant suddenly, especially without medical supervision. Withdrawal effects such as dizziness, nausea, sweating, anxiety, tremor and confusion can occur, not to mention relapse of your symptoms. When you and your doctor decide you've sufficiently recovered, most of you should be able to cease taking antidepressants, but this must happen slowly, with gradual dose tapering over one to two weeks.

- at the risk of repeating ourselves, antidepressants should be used in combination with talking therapies and other forms of support, not as a substitute.

Antidepressants in pregnancy — A discussion about risk

Ponder for a moment the wonders and complexities of human development: from an embryo — a small collection of cells — we can grow a living, breathing human being in only nine months. It's a miracle that happens every minute of every day, but it's a miracle nonetheless.

If you think of it in these terms, it's less surprising to consider that sometimes things go awry during pregnancy. Even if you do everything right — avoid alcohol and cigarettes; eat healthy foods, but not soft cheeses or raw fish that may be infected with listeria; exercise, but not too hard; avoid hot tubs etc — there is still the chance that you may have a baby with health or development problems.

Overall, for a typical pregnancy, the chance of you having a baby with a birth defect is in the range of *2 in 100 to 4 in 100*.[2] Some of these birth defects will be minor; others, unfortunately, not so minor. The point we are making is that no pregnancy is without risk. (Two authors of this book know this only too well, each having a child with an autism spectrum disorder).

Research suggests that most of the antidepressants do not increase the risk of birth defects above the normal range; that is *2 in 100 to 4 in 100*.

In summary, doctors cannot guarantee that if you are taking an antidepressant during pregnancy your baby will be born perfectly well, just as doctors cannot guarantee that a baby born to a woman who is not taking any medication will be born perfectly well. Nonetheless, the information we have regarding birth defects and antidepressants is, for the most part, reassuring. Many women find they are able to relax more after their 19-week ultrasound.

There are occasionally other complications from antidepressants, mainly associated with their use in late pregnancy, and your doctor will need to discuss the risk of these and their management with you.

Wherever possible, doctors will avoid prescribing medication for you during pregnancy, especially early pregnancy. However, as we explained above, sometimes the risks of not treating are greater.

An excellent resource is Dr Shoshana Bennett's book, *Pregnant on Prozac: The Essential Guide to Making the Best Decision for You and Your Baby* (GPP Life, 2009) This consumer-friendly book explains the pros and cons of antidepressants in pregnancy in much more detail than we are able to go into here.

Closer to home, the **Black Dog Institute** has a fact sheet called *Safety of Antidepressants in Pregnancy and Breastfeeding*. Go to their website and follow the *Depression Fact Sheet* links. There is also a fact sheet: *Treatments for Bipolar Disorder During Pregnancy and the Postnatal Period*.

You can also consult **Motherisk**, a Canadian-based pregnancy and breastfeeding information service, located at the Hospital for Sick Children in Toronto. **www.motherisk.org/women/index.jsp**

However, none of these resources should be considered a substitute for careful consultation with your prescribing doctor.

Antidepressants and breastfeeding

When it comes to breastfeeding, the path is less complicated. The majority of antidepressants — with a couple of exceptions — pass into the breast milk in very small amounts and are regarded as compatible with breastfeeding. So, if you enjoy breastfeeding and your baby is healthy, you will most likely be able to continue nursing your baby with some peace of mind.

Alternatively, if you feel uncomfortable taking any medication whilst breastfeeding, you might want to talk to your doctor about weaning before starting treatment. However, if you do decide to wean, this should be done gradually.

There are no rights or wrongs here. Whatever decision you make, just make sure it is one that you are most comfortable with.

PANDA have produced an excellent fact sheet, called *Postnatal depression and breastfeeding*, which summarises the issues around breastfeeding really well. You can download this from the PANDA website: www.panda.org.au.

Table1. Antidepressants for perinatal anxiety and depression[1-7]

Medication	How they work	Some side effects	Use in pregnancy	Use in breastfeeding[†]
Selective serotonin reuptake inhibitors **SSRIs** eg fluoxetine sertraline citalopram escitalopram paroxetine	Selectively block the re-absorption (*reuptake*) of serotonin by certain nerve cells in the brain, increasing levels of serotonin and improving mood.	Nausea, restlessness, insomnia, drowsiness, dry mouth, diarrhoea, dizziness, headache, sexual dysfunction, interactions with other medicines.	SSRIs do not appear to increase the rate of birth defects above normal levels. Some early studies suggested that paroxetine, given in early pregnancy, may increase the risk of heart defects, although later studies have not found a link. SSRIs may slightly increase the risk of early miscarriage, from about 9% to 12%. They may also increase the risk of premature birth and low birth weight babies; however untreated depression also appears to increase these risks. Withdrawal symptoms (eg jitteriness, poor muscle tone, weak cry) have been reported in infants after their mothers have used SSRIs in late pregnancy. Symptoms are mainly mild and short-lived. Babies require closer monitoring for a few days after birth. Some studies suggest SSRIs may increase the risk of an extremely rare lung disorder, persistent pulmonary hypertension of the newborn, although this is yet to be confirmed.	Very low levels of SSRIs enter the breast milk. Can generally be taken whilst breastfeeding, although sertraline and paroxetine (if commenced postnatally) may be preferred). Monitor infant for side effects.

Medication	How they work	Some side effects	Use in pregnancy	Use in breastfeeding†
Serotonin-noradrenaline reuptake inhibitors **SNRIs** eg venlafaxine	Inhibits serotonin and noradrenaline re-absorption, leading to increased brain levels of these neurotransmitters.	Nausea, vomiting, loss of appetite, headache, sweating, rash, dizziness, fatigue, tremor, high blood pressure, interactions with other medicines.	Like the SSRIs, venlafaxine does not appear to increase the rate of birth defects above normal levels.\n\nWhen used in late pregnancy withdrawal symptoms in newborn may result (see above).	A moderate amount of venlafaxine enters the breast milk. Other antidepressants are generally preferred. If used, monitor for side effects.
Mirtazapine	Acts in the brain to increase both noradrenaline and serotonin levels.	Increased appetite, weight gain, sedation, weakness, peripheral oedema (swelling of limbs), interactions with other medicines.	Studies suggest mirtazapine does not increase birth defects above normal levels.	Can generally be taken whilst breastfeeding. Monitor for side effects.

Medication	How they work	Some side effects	Use in pregnancy	Use in breastfeeding[†]
Tricyclic anti-depressants eg amitriptyline nortriptyline clomipramine doxepin dothiepin imipramine	This older family of antidepressants block reabsorption of noradrenaline and serotonin in the brain.	Sedation, dry mouth, blurred vision, decreased tear production, constipation, weight gain, *postural hypotension* (low blood pressure when a person stands up), rapid heart rate, tremor, dizziness, sweating, agitation, insomnia, interactions with other medicines.	Wide experience suggests that tricyclic antidepressants do not increase the risk of birth defects. As with other antidepressants, some babies whose mothers have taken tricyclic antidepressants up until delivery have shown symptoms of withdrawal.	Tricyclic anti-depressants, with the exception of doxepin, can generally be taken whilst breast feeding. Nortriptyline is considered first-choice. Monitor for side effects.

† For healthy, full term babies. Specialist advice is required for infants who are premature, low birth weight or unwell.

Other medications used for perinatal mental health disorders

Benzodiazepines are used to treat anxiety and insomnia, although their long-term use is discouraged, as tolerance to their effects and dependence can develop. Some commonly known benzodiazepines are lorazepam, temazepam and alprazolam. Benzodiazepines have a limited place in the treatment of perinatal anxiety; their use is restricted to cases of severe anxiety, while waiting for a prescribed antidepressant to take effect.

Benzodiazepines do have the advantage that they can be taken on an 'as needed' basis, unlike antidepressants, which you have to take every day (but that is probably their only advantage).

Older studies suggest that benzodiazepines may increase the risk of cleft palate if taken during the first trimester of pregnancy; however, more recent studies have not found a link.[2, 4] If taken in high doses during late pregnancy, benzodiazepines may affect the newborn infant, sometimes causing low Apgar scores at birth and mild withdrawal symptoms. If required, some benzodiazepines can be taken whilst you are breastfeeding but babies may need to be observed for signs of over sleepiness.

Mood stabilisers are commonly used in the treatment of bipolar disorder. Since this condition usually includes episodes of both mania and depression, often more than one medication is necessary to control symptoms. Well known mood stabilisers include lithium and the *anticonvulsants* (medicines first developed for the treatment of epilepsy) carbamazepine, sodium valproate and lamotrigine.

Antipsychotics are medications primarily (but not exclusively) used to manage psychosis eg delusions or hallucinations.

There are two main groups of antipsychotics:
- *typical antipsychotics*, eg haloperidol or chlorpromazine
- *atypical antipsychotics*, such as risperidone, olanzapine, quetiapine and aripiprazole.

Antipsychotics are generally reserved for women suffering more serious perinatal mental health disorders, such as puerperal psychosis or bipolar disorder, although they are occasionally used to *augment* (boost) the effects of antidepressant therapy in cases of very severe depression. Women with pre-existing mental health disorders, such as schizophrenia, may also require treatment with antipsychotics during pregnancy and the postnatal period. Untreated psychosis poses a particular risk to mother and baby because — as a consequence of her illness — the mother's judgement will be impaired.

The medical management of these conditions is challenging and unfortunately beyond the scope of this book. Psychiatrist involvement is essential at this time, and in many cases hospitalisation may be required.

The Black Dog Institute has produced a fact sheet, *Treatments for bipolar disorder during pregnancy and the postnatal period,* which can be downloaded from their website.

Although not a medication, it's worth mentioning that **electroconvulsive therapy (ECT)** is very occasionally used to treat severe cases of perinatal mental health disorders, although only when all other avenues have been exhausted and the risk from symptoms (such as psychosis or strong suicidal urges) outweighs those of treatment.[2]

ECT takes only a few seconds, with the patient first sedated with a short-acting anaesthetic. Unfortunately, ECT has had an image problem since the movie *One Flew Over the Cuckoo's Nest* came out, but with advances in anaesthesia and monitoring in recent years, it is now generally regarded an effective and well-tolerated treatment in resistant cases.

Antidepressants — myths and realities

I had previously been resistant to taking antidepressant medication... I went to see a doctor, and when he asked I said

I was prepared to take the tablets. The first medication I took was reasonably effective, but I later had to change... The medication I am on has no significant side effects for me, and it has allowed me to get well enough to do all sorts of things I needed to do anyway.

If, like most of us, you read the paper, watch TV and browse the internet you've probably come across worrying information about antidepressants from time to time. However, not all the information you read is likely to be accurate. We need to deal with a few common questions right now.

Will antidepressants change my personality?

Depression and anxiety have *already* changed your personality. What doctors are aiming to achieve with antidepressant treatment is to make you feel more like your *old* self — lifting your mood and quelling the worst of those negative thoughts — so you can get to work on the things, such as talking therapies and getting the right support, that will make life better in the long run.

Will I become addicted to antidepressants?

No, antidepressants are not addictive.

Will I get side effects?

All medicines have side effects and antidepressants are no exception: we list some of the common ones in Table 1. However, not *all* people taking antidepressants will experience side effects — you may be one of the lucky ones who doesn't. Moreover, lots of these side effects are mild and short-lived, generally resolving within a few days, or at worst, a few weeks. Your doctor will tell you what side effects to look out for and, of these, which are the ones that you really need to worry about.

What if I am already taking an antidepressant when I find out I am pregnant?

Women who are already taking antidepressants and other medications for mental health disorders frequently stop their medications once they find out they're pregnant because of concerns about the effects of medication on the developing baby. Unfortunately it's estimated that about 70% of these women will suffer a relapse in symptoms.[1] That's why it's vitally important you do not stop any medicine without informing a health care professional of your intentions — you will need to be closely observed for signs of relapse.

Aren't antidepressants just a crutch?

A crutch is something that supports you until you get back on your feet again. Is that such a bad thing? Antidepressants can help by restoring your 'brain chemistry' so that you can get back on your psychological feet again. Once well enough, you should be able to get rid of the crutch, and wean slowly off your medication.

Am I a failure for needing to take antidepressants?

There remains a stigma in our society about taking medications for anxiety and depression. Whilst few people would think twice about taking medicine to help manage their asthma or diabetes, somehow the same attitudes don't apply when our mental health is involved. If there are medications that can help restore your ability to think clearly and function better, why should you feel a failure for taking them, especially if only temporarily? Fortunately celebrities such as Brooke Shields and, closer to home, Jessica Rowe, are now helping to dispel the negative stereotypes.

COMPLEMENTARY AND ALTERNATIVE THERAPIES

It's natural for us to want to exert some control over our own destiny and for many of us that means seeking out complementary and alternative therapies for health and medical conditions — perinatal depression and anxiety being no exception.

The days of 'doctor always knows best' are gone. That is a good thing, *mostly*.

Following is a brief review of some of the complementary and alternative therapies that have been used in the management of depression and anxiety (most information being for the former). However, before we continue, it's worth issuing a few words of warning.

Beware what you read on the internet!

The internet is a virtual treasure trove of health information these days, but not all of it is of equal merit. It's a good idea to seek out sites supported by government or educational institutions (which usually have 'gov' or 'edu' rather than 'com' in their URL) or those of not-for-profit health organisations, such as *beyondblue* and the Black Dog Institute.

You may encounter glossy websites promising quick fixes for anxiety and depression — 'drug-free' is a favoured term. Commonly these will be backed up by lots of glowing testimonials, but no real scientific evidence. Please be wary, especially if the treatment requires that you hand over large amounts of cash up front. If it sounds too good to be true, it probably is.

In general, try to be sceptical about any information that seems too 'black and white'. Scientists almost never talk in absolutes; their scientific training teaches them to qualify and question, and talk about pros and cons. If you stumble across material that seems overly positive about a therapy — or, alternatively, overly negative (some religious groups are opposed to the use of antidepressants) — question it, as there may be a hidden agenda behind it.

Natural does not equal safe.

There is a tendency in our society to equate the terms 'safe' and 'natural', as if the two things necessarily go together. Some of the most toxic prescription medicines we use today — the heart medicine, digoxin, from the foxglove plant; morphine from the opium poppy, for example — are derived from natural plant sources.

Natural therapies are *not* automatically safe. Of course, if you seek out complementary therapies that are physical in nature, such as massage, in most instances that's likely to be ok. However, please talk to your doctor before taking any herbal or nutritional supplements, such as St John's Wort (see page 132). This advice is important if you are breastfeeding and *essential* if you are pregnant. Few of these supplements have been adequately tested in pregnancy and we do not yet know if they are safe.

For the purposes of this book, we will define a complementary therapy as one that is used together with a conventional treatment. In contrast, an alternative therapy is used in place of conventional treatment. However, in practice the terms are often used interchangeably.

Of the complementary and alternative therapies used for anxiety and depression, the following show particular promise:

Omega-3 fatty acids

These polyunsaturated fatty acids probably need no introduction. Omega-3s have widely established health benefits, especially with respect to heart disease. The good news is: two omega-3 fatty acids eicosapentaenoic acid (EPA) and docosahexaenoic acid (DHA), present in oily fish, have been found to alleviate depression in a number of studies, most commonly when used in combination with an antidepressant.[8]

EPA and DHA are also regarded as important for nervous system development in the foetus and the infant. Because of the potential benefits for both mother and infant, there has been particular interest in their role in perinatal depression.

Talk to your doctor about taking omega-3 supplements. When looking for a supplement, try to find a good quality product; your doctor may be able to advise you.

Moderate fish intake is also considered safe, just as long as the following warnings from Food Standards Australia New Zealand are adhered to:

Because of concerns regarding mercury, pregnant women,
women planning pregnancy and young children should limit

their consumption of shark (flake), broadbill, marlin and swordfish to no more than one serve per fortnight; and orange roughy (sea perch) and catfish to no more than one serve per week, with no other fish being consumed during these time periods. Other fish, including salmon and tuna can be eaten two to three times a week.[9]

The Black Dog Institute has produced an excellent fact sheet: *Omega-3 and mood disorders*, which is free to download from their website. Go to **www.blackdoginstitute.org.au.**

St John's Wort

Also called *hypericum*, St John's Wort is a herbal remedy that has been widely used in the treatment of depression. It appears to be effective in mild to moderate depression, although not in more severe cases. Whilst many would prefer to take an herbal supplement over a prescribed antidepressant, St John's Wort is not without its problems. In particular, it has several drug interactions with prescription medicines and should not be taken with other antidepressants, as serious reactions may occur. It can also interact with the oral contraceptive pill; unplanned pregnancies have resulted.[8]

There is also, of course, the question mark over its use in pregnancy and lactation. *Unfortunately we currently do not have sufficient data to indicate that it is safe, so St John's Wort should not be used if you're pregnant or breastfeeding.*

The Black Dog Institute has also produced a fact sheet on St John's Wort, although this does not specifically refer to its use in pregnancy and/or breastfeeding. Go to **www.blackdoginstitute.org.au.**

Folate

There is growing evidence that folate (also known as folic acid) may help prevent and treat depression; although most commonly it has been used to augment the effects of antidepressant therapy rather than by itself. Researchers are also still unclear as to which people are most likely to benefit from folate, and what is the best dose to use.[8]

Folate is a water-soluble B vitamin that is found naturally in foods such as leafy green vegetables. Our bodies require folate to make and maintain new cells. Of course, women are recommended to take folate supplements prior to and during pregnancy (at least 400 micrograms), as there is research showing that supplementation reduces the risk of neural tube defects (malformations of the spine, brain and skull). In September 2009, it became a legal requirement in Australia that all bread-making flour, except organic flour, contain added folic acid. As a result, most bread now contains added folic acid.

Talk to your doctor about the need for extra folate, but if you decide to take a multivitamin supplement make sure it's one that is suitable to take during pregnancy and lactation — not all are.

Bright light therapy

Light affects mood, energy and circadian rhythms, and its therapeutic effects have received quite a bit of attention in recent years.

The mechanism by which light therapy exerts an antidepressant effect is not completely known, but it's an established treatment for *seasonal affective disorder* (a type of depression associated with lack of natural light during the winter months) and recent studies suggest promising results in pregnant women and new mothers.[8]

To utilise light therapy, you are required to sit in front of a special, downward-tilted light box, which is placed about 30 centimetres from your eyes. You can read, eat or engage in other activities, just as long as you remain in front of the box. Depending on your individual needs, sessions will vary in time (up to about 30 minutes) and frequency (days per week).

Light therapy is not without side effects, such as nausea, jitteriness and headache. More importantly, light therapy can induce mania in people with bipolar disorder, so it *should not* be commenced without medical supervision.

A useful website to learn more about bright light therapy is the Center for Environmental Therapeutics. Visit **www.cet.org.**

S-Adenosyl Methionine

SAMe, as it is commonly known, is a molecule that occurs naturally and is important in human metabolism. Its antidepressant effect is thought to be due to its influence on the metabolism of important neurotransmitters, such as serotonin and dopamine, in the central nervous system. In clinical trials SAMe has been administered orally and by injection and has been found to be effective as an alternative to the older tricyclic antidepressants, although not all patients respond to treatment.[8]

Supplements can be purchased from pharmacies and health food stores. Generally SAMe appears to be well tolerated, with gastrointestinal complaints and headaches the most commonly reported side effects. However, there are concerns that SAMe may provoke manic episodes in people with bipolar disorder. While a small number of pregnant women have taken SAMe for liver disease in the past, very little is known about its use in pregnancy and breastfeeding. It is essential you talk to your doctor before considering treatment.

Acupuncture

Acupuncture is a traditional Chinese method of healing that uses fine needles in specific points in the body, which the Chinese theorise corrects imbalances in the flow of energy in the body. According to Western medicine, it may stimulate nerves, resulting in the release of neurotransmitters in the brain. There are question marks over the effectiveness of acupuncture as a treatment for anxiety and depression, because the clinical trials which have found a benefit have been of an inconsistent, but generally poor, quality.[8]

Acupuncture is generally considered a low risk treatment, with little risk of adverse effects. However, pregnant women need to be extra cautious and only work with experienced practitioners, as some acupuncture points may cause uterine stimulation, potentially speeding up labour.[10]

Exercise

As hard as it is to muster up the motivation and energy to actually do it, exercise is a big help in my mood and the way I cope. More so if I do it regularly and consistently.

There is research to suggest that regular exercise of moderate intensity may alleviate the symptoms of mild to moderate depression. The Black Dog Institute has produced a comprehensive fact sheet on the benefits of exercise and depression.

Brisk walking has been found to be beneficial for depression, so even an energetic walk pushing the pram may help. One study found that group pram walking sessions may be helpful in postnatal depression.[11]

The rest

Other complementary therapies have less scientific research to support their use in anxiety and depression. These include aromatherapy, massage, most herbal supplements, homeopathy, chiropractic treatment, yoga, hypnotherapy and spiritual and energy healing. This does not necessarily mean they don't work; it may mean that studies haven't been done in sufficient numbers and/ or quality to establish that they do. Even when testing mainstream treatments such as antidepressants, conducting good quality trials in depression is difficult. There are no 100% foolproof tests that allow doctors to diagnose and assess progress, and recruiting sufficient numbers of patients who will be compliant with treatment can be difficult.

Therefore, we are not saying it's not worth trying some of these complementary therapies — bearing in mind our warning about herbal supplements in pregnancy and breastfeeding. After all, it's unlikely you're going to feel more stressed and anxious after a massage! We do, however, recommend that you do not rely on them exclusively and thus use them in lieu of more proven treatments, such as psychological therapies and medication (if deemed necessary). Also, it's really important you seek out practitioners with experience in treating patients who either are pregnant or breastfeeding.

Unfortunately, we do not have time to go into all the many and varied complementary therapies that have been touted as treatments for perinatal anxiety and depression. However, *beyondblue* have produced some great resources to help the lay person assess the scientific evidence supporting the many different therapies — mainstream and alternative — for both anxiety and depression. These publications are called: *A Guide to What Works for Depression* and *A Guide to What Works for Anxiety Disorders* and are available to download from the *beyondblue* website, under the *Get Information* tab. We'd recommend you check them out.

8
MY RECOVERY — HOW WE GOT BETTER

I had postnatal depression after my daughter was born 6½ years ago, although looking back now I can see that I also had antenatal depression. While some of the content in my story is quite distressing, it's really important to know that I was at the very severe end of the perinatal depression spectrum, and not everyone who experiences this will think or feel the way I did. It's also important to know that, as unwell as I was, I got better.

Before I had my baby, I completed a university degree with Honours in Psychology and had a great job (totally unrelated to my degree!) with lots of responsibility. I was managing a team of people and earning good money. I was capable, competent, and confident in my abilities. Then, at the age of 30, I had a baby, and my world fell apart.

My first pregnancy ended in miscarriage at eight weeks, and although it was early, I really felt it as a huge loss. I have Type 2 Diabetes, although at the time it was borderline and my diabetic-

specialist obstetrician assured me it was not related to the miscarriage, someone asked me if I would look after my blood sugar better next time so that it (miscarriage) wouldn't happen again. That planted the seed of doubt and anxiety in my mind that I was responsible for the miscarriage, even though rationally, I knew I wasn't.

I fell pregnant again about three months later and the anxiety started about ten minutes after I got that positive result — if there was anything wrong with my baby it would be entirely my fault. As it turned out, the pregnancy went well despite the diabetes and insulin injections, my blood sugar was well controlled and my baby was perfect.

Emotionally however, I wasn't well at all. I was terrified of giving birth — convinced that if I had an epidural I would end up paralysed, or would die if I had a c-section. I had had poorly managed depression and anxiety in the past and was on antidepressants prior to getting pregnant. I took myself off them to prevent any risk to the baby but didn't tell my doctor as I didn't think it was important. I thought I was fine, and any emotion I felt was just hormones, a normal part of being pregnant. But it wasn't normal at all.

After she was born, I felt elated for the first day or so, then I crashed. She wasn't even 48 hours old, and I couldn't stop crying. I told one of the midwives that I was crying all the time. She told me that I was a mother now, and I wouldn't be normal if I didn't feel some emotion. She was the one that I had told about my history of depression. She missed the point.

Breastfeeding wasn't going well. I was getting conflicting information from the midwives and getting more and more distressed. By the time I went home from hospital, I still couldn't get my baby to attach and my milk hadn't come in. They gave me 20ml of formula in a little plastic bottle, enough for one feed, with

*no teat. I went home with a four-day old baby, and I had no way
to feed her. It didn't get any better from there.*

*Having been so competent in my professional life, everything
I thought and knew about myself was shattered by the arrival
of this tiny little person. I couldn't get her to go to sleep and I
couldn't feed her as I had planned and expected I would do. I
felt like I was a complete and utter failure as a mother, and as a
woman. Breastfeeding became a real issue for me. I spent a couple
of days at a breastfeeding clinic, and things would be fine while I
was there, but when I got home, it wouldn't work.*

*The first day I was at the clinic, when my baby was eight days old,
I cried almost the whole time. The midwife called my obstetrician
(OB), and said 'I think we've got puerperal psychosis here'. He
put me back on my antidepressants immediately and referred me
to a psychiatrist who I was to see the following week. He also
asked me to come in and see him a couple of days later.*

*While I was in his office, he and his midwife talked to me, but I
couldn't understand a word they said. I knew it was English, but
it might as well have been another language — it was all garbled,
like the words were all mixed up. That day I had what I refer to as
my first 'brush with psychosis'. It could have even been starting in
the OB's office. My baby was ten days old.*

*When we got home, I crawled in to my bed and refused to get up.
I couldn't sleep but I wasn't really awake, it was like a strange in-
between place. I was incredibly anxious, and the words puerperal
psychosis went around and around in my head, over and over. I
tossed and turned, and thrashed around in bed. I felt dizzy and
couldn't think straight. I kept wishing that I had 'just stuck with
my cats'. There are a few hours that night that I don't remember.
Apparently I told my husband to call an ambulance if things got
bad.*

I wouldn't respond to my baby, and I was terrified of her. My Mum and husband had to care for her. At about midnight, after almost 12 hours, I finally got out of bed. I still couldn't feed or hold my baby, but felt I should at least be there while my husband did.

Over the next few weeks the anxiety got worse. I couldn't eat because of the feeling of constriction in my throat, so I lived on Sustagen, water and juice, and lost a lot of weight.

Breastfeeding continued to be a problem, so I ended up expressing and bottlefeeding for eight weeks, supplementing with formula. I didn't have much of a supply, so I called the ABA helpline for advice. The counsellor suggested that I express more often, every couple of hours, for a few days. I took her literally, and expressed for 10–30 minutes, every two hours around the clock for almost five days. It made no difference to my milk supply, but I was incredibly sleep deprived and becoming more unwell as a result. On top of that, I was washing and sterilizing bottles, making formula, feeding the baby and trying to settle her. I was spending 16 hours each day on feeding-related activities alone. It was crazy.

During this time I went three days without having a shower, simply because I couldn't find the time to have one. When I finally did, it was 2am and I cried the whole time, distressed about how horrible my life had become — I couldn't imagine it ever getting better. I now understand that anxiety and sleep deprivation both contributed to poor milk supply, but nobody ever offered me any other options for increasing it.

My husband was so concerned about what was happening, that he begged me to stop expressing and just formula feed. I eventually gave in when my baby was eight weeks old, and I once again felt like a complete and total failure. I felt so guilty about not being able to give her the 'best start in life', and I worried that going on to formula would result in her being obese, allergic to everything, asthmatic, and having a below-average IQ. I started to panic that the formula was toxic. I thought I was the worst mother in the world for feeding it to her and I hated myself for it.

At the first session of the new mums' group run by the local early childhood nurse (when my baby was about 11 weeks old), there were 32 new mums in the room. One of the nurses asked who was still breastfeeding, and applauded the mums that raised their hands, 'Bravo girls, well done' she said, clapping.

I wanted to stand up and say 'And who really wanted to breastfeed but can't and feels like a useless piece of crap?' But I didn't. I wish I had.

I had been seeing the psychiatrist for a few weeks, but he was based in the city, and it was just too far from where I lived. After one visit I asked him if I could possibly have a nap somewhere before driving home (I figured the building was full of psychiatrists, there had to be a spare couch somewhere), but that wasn't possible. I found myself driving off the freeway onto the median strip on the way home, I assume I had dozed off, so I didn't go back to see him. I planned to find someone closer to home. By that point I was up to 150mg of Effexor.

When my baby was about nine weeks old, I had my lowest, most dangerous day yet. I was giving her a bath, and thought 'if I just walked away, I could be free'. I thought about letting her drown. I was so horrified, I fell in a heap on the bathroom floor and howled. I wanted to kill myself. I had been having a lot of intrusive morbid and suicidal thoughts for a few weeks, but this was the worst so far. I thought if I killed myself, my husband could find someone else, someone better. I thought that he deserved a better wife, and my baby deserved a better mother.

Terrified, I started calling every helpline I could find. PANDA wasn't open that day, so I made contact with a similar helpline from Sydney (which is no longer running). They called me every day for a couple of weeks. I also contacted the Postnatal Depression Counsellor who was based at the local Community Health Centre, but she wasn't there so I left a message on her machine. She later told me it was lucky that I left my name and phone number first, because she couldn't understand another word of the minute-long message that I left.

The counsellor came to visit me at home weekly for the next few weeks. By the fourth visit, she was alarmed at how far I had deteriorated, so she got straight on the phone to my GP and a private mother baby unit (MBU), and arranged for my admission the following day. They didn't actually have a bed in the MBU at the time, so I initially went into the maternity ward, purely because of how unwell I was and how hard the counsellor pushed to get me in there. I was lucky they took me so quickly. My baby was 14 weeks old.

I was so afraid of being hospitalised. I thought I was going mad, that they would lock me up and take my baby away, and that I would never get better. But when my counsellor came that day and took charge, I just felt so relieved that someone knew what to do. I really believe that she saved my life, and possibly my baby's life as well.

My husband was at work while all of this was being arranged. I called to tell him what was happening. I cried and apologised to him, saying 'I am so sorry, it wasn't supposed to be like this'. His answer was 'We will do what we have to, and we will do it together'.

I was in the MBU for five weeks the first time, and while I wasn't cured, it was exactly where I needed to be at that time. The staff taught me so much about managing my baby. I had daily visits from my hospital-based psychiatrist who quickly increased my Effexor to 375mg. The daily group sessions were really helpful, as was meeting other mothers who also had postnatal depression. Some of the women that I met were having ECT and had been there for months, while others would come and go after just a few days.

After my discharge, I attended a weekly out-patient therapy group for about three months. I found it very helpful, and made some great friendships as well. When that group finished I started attending the local postnatal depression support group that was run by my counsellor. That was a life changing experience.

My husband and I had moved to a new town while I was pregnant, and by the time our baby came, we still didn't know anyone, so I was totally isolated. This was a big issue for me. Our families lived hours away so I had no form of support, or social or adult contact. Going to the group I met other women who were at various places in their recoveries. I felt welcome from the first day, and I continued going for the three years that it took me to recover. I formed friendships that I still have today — we share a special bond. I still go to the group, but for the last three years it's been as a mentor to other mums.

I had two more admissions to the MBU in the months following the initial stay. One of them was to help with my baby who had developed silent reflux at around 8–10 weeks and didn't sleep for more than 40 minutes at a time. She struggled to feed because of the pain that she had, and would scream whenever she saw a bottle coming. Each feed would take an hour and we would both cry the whole time. I was highly anxious about her feeding and sleeping, and became very unwell again. We tried various formulas to no avail. At one point my MCHN said 'she must just really hate milk.' It was my counsellor who actually identified the symptoms of silent reflux, and after the diagnosis was made, we went back to the MBU and my baby was put on a medication called Zantac. This made a huge difference, and at six months, she was finally able to feed and sleep 'normally'. It was at this point, one afternoon in the MBU, that I finally felt a rush of love for her.

You hear mothers say that they fell in love with their babies the moment they first saw them. I loved her while I was pregnant, but after she was born, I didn't really feel it. I was very protective, I cared for and about her, and worried about her a lot, but I don't think it was love. I think I was so anxious, and depressed, and stressed, that there just wasn't room for love.

I felt like I had made a huge mistake and ruined my life. I knew it wasn't her fault, but I resented the fact that my life was so completely different now. So that day, when I finally felt a rush of love, was amazing.

She, on the other hand, was a very happy, social baby who smiled for the first time at three-and-a-half weeks, and then just kept on smiling. Despite how bad I felt, I would concentrate on making eye contact with her, smiling and singing to her, then when she was in bed I would collapse from the effort. She had no idea what was going on with her mummy, and I did my best to make sure that if I couldn't smile back at her, there would be someone in the house who could. I was very fortunate to have the support of my parents.

My recovery took about three years. I had ups and downs, but the anxiety finally left me after about eight or nine months and I settled into a 'routine' of depression with regular visits for counselling with my new local psychiatrist, and with my counsellor.

During those first few months, I had several more episodes of severe anxiety when I would shut down and be unable and unwilling to look after my baby, sometimes for days at a time. Every little noise she made was enough to trigger such intense anxiety that I would seize up and be incapable of speech, let alone doing anything functional. I would put earplugs in, take sedatives to knock myself out for a few hours, and sleep on the couch in the same room where all the action was — I wanted to be physically present, but I didn't want to know about any of it. My husband would have to take time off work, and my parents often came and stayed at our place to help.

During these times of intense anxiety, I would sometimes behave strangely, and was often very confused. One day I called my husband who was at home with the baby, in a blind panic because I didn't know where I was or what I was doing. I had apparently gone to do the grocery shopping and was standing in the middle of Coles having a total meltdown. I couldn't remember getting there. Another time I called the manager at the same Coles and absolutely went off my head, because there were seeds in my seedless watermelon. I remember that episode.

During these times I would think about ways to kill myself, and had a few plans in mind. There are hours and days of which I have no memory at all.

My doctors thought that I had experienced severe hormone withdrawal following the birth that 'scrambled my brain chemistry', but they didn't want to risk treating me with any sort of hormone therapy because not enough is understood about it. So I stayed on my antidepressants and had to 'ride it out'. Both my hospital-based psychiatrist and perinatal depression counsellor (who had never met each other by the way), told me that in the 20-odd years they had each been treating women, they had never seen anyone so severely impacted by their hormones. Lucky me! I have since had correspondence with a Professor in the UK who believes that I had a bout of postnatal psychosis on that tenth day, followed by approximately eight bouts of menstrual psychosis, which happens to about 1 in 10,000 women.

There was later suggestion of posttraumatic stress disorder as a result of my early postnatal depression experience. My psychiatrist also diagnosed a form of bipolar disorder, bipolar 2, as a result of the experience. I still have ups and downs, and while my downs can be quite severe and last for several weeks, I batten down the hatches and call on my supports to make sure that my daughter is ok. I don't ever become fully manic though — it's more like being more energetic and talkative than normal, and I sleep a bit less. I wonder though, if I actually had bipolar 2 before I had my baby, which would have contributed to the development and severity of my condition.

I left my old job nearly four years ago and used some of the payout to fund a course — a Diploma in Counselling. I contacted PANDA (see page 275) and did the training course to become a volunteer telephone support worker. A few months later I filled in for a few weeks doing administration at PANDA, and those few weeks turned into almost two years. I resigned from that role late last year to concentrate on completing my study and gaining my counselling qualification.

Recently I went back to volunteering on the phones and I love it. I will soon be working in a paid counselling role which I am very excited about. I am also an official volunteer with the local Community Health Centre working in post- and antenatal depression support, with my counsellor. I hope to specialise in that area of counselling. I never had a passion before, but I have one now.

I had a truly horrible introduction to motherhood in my experience of postnatal depression, and I have come out the other end a different person, a better person. I am stronger now, and more independent than I have ever been.

The key to recovery is getting help, and getting it quickly. If you don't feel good, talk to someone about it — your partner, friends, family, GP, MCHN, PANDA. Look at your options on the bio-psycho-social model. Consider medication, counselling, and/or support groups, and feel better.

I saw a psychologist but was never given the diagnosis of postnatal depression, just anxiety. I found that my anxiety was never taken in the context of having just had a major life transition.

Counselling and talking was worth a truckload in pills — medication never worked for me. What helped the most was talking, talking, talking — being open to feeling the painful issues, being ready to accept that being a vulnerable human being is ok.

I only became 'me' since having children — prior to this I was a shadow of myself — an unwrapped gift, unsure of and unaccepting of most aspects of me. I have only 'grown up' in the last few years — my children have given me the gift of understanding myself.

Its not 'why me?' any more — life just is what it is and now it is 'well, why not me?'

I went to the GP, who luckily specialises in women's health and knows a lot about depression. She gave me the Edinburgh test and told me that I had postnatal depression. She then gave me a referral to a residential early parenting program and a prescription for antidepressants.

Were the drugs helpful? Maybe, maybe not. I was never really sure. The residential stay was a mixture of helpful and unhelpful, one week was good, the next week there were different staff who were not so good. Some really knew what they were doing and made a real effort to help and to find out what was the best way to help me through what was happening. Others did not seem to really have an understanding of what postnatal depression was and basically felt that you had to 'get on with it'. I got a real mixed bag.

They and the GP then referred me to St John of God, who offered me a place on a new day program. This was run by a psychiatrist, nurses and social workers, you attended one day a week and it was run like a playgroup/mothers' group, with group work and individual consultations with the psychiatrist. I felt it was a 'getting to know your baby', but by this stage Clare was about five and a half months old and I was due to go back to work in a month, so although very good for me, it was a bit 'too little too late'.

Although I was only diagnosed and treated for antenatal depression once, I believe I had some degree of dysthymia in the first trimester of all of my pregnancies. I would struggle to leave the house, vomited till at least 13 weeks, and generally felt low in mood. However, I felt great in the second and third trimesters, and beyond some early parenting anxiety I don't believe I suffered from postnatal depression, not severely anyway.

There is a good chance that my diagnosed depression was a reactive type. At the time I was pregnant for the fifth time in five years. I had had two early miscarriages, lost a baby at six months and I had two children under three. I was exhausted, I was anaemic and I was severely nauseated around the clock. We had moved three times in the last three years, including one year overseas and another move was on the cards. We had several family crises during this time and I was facing losses I wasn't able to manage. I had never asked for help; it was not my family's way (lots of pride in 'doing it tough').

It felt like my life was caving in, I had taken on too much and there was no way out. I considered termination on a daily basis. I also felt abandoned and didn't seem to be feeling any emotions related to the people around me. Eventually my love for my children was numbed: I knew I loved them but I couldn't feel it. This was what finally alarmed my husband into action.

The world had taken on a two dimensional quality and I didn't feel real. I felt unable to care for my children. I spent as much time in bed as I could. I went to bed each night around seven; as soon as the girls were in bed. I was unable to leave the house, unable to eat, unable to cook.

I started having early morning wakening and eventually complete insomnia. I wandered the house at night checking that the girls were all right.

I remember little of how I managed to care for my daughters apart from lying on the couch while they watched videos. I remember being ok if my husband was around but becoming severely anxious when he would have to go back to work.

This was all completely out of character for me. I began to wonder what life for my family would be like without me. I didn't feel present anyway. It dawned on me that this must be depression.

At 13 weeks I saw my GP. He encouraged me to put some lifestyle measures in place. Because I suspected I had perinatal depression, I became quite panicked about delaying treatment. I became severely agitated, had invasive negative thoughts and knew that there was no option but to get medical help.

I became almost suicidal within a day of starting my first selective serotonin reuptake inhibitors (SSRIs). I felt so ill, almost as if I would explode or implode. I felt that someone would have to either kill me or take my baby out of me.

I tried another SSRI and this was hideous. All my symptoms worsened: nausea, vomiting, acute diarrhoea, and anxiety. It was a slow hell, but I was determined to do the right thing and get better. After ten weeks I finally got to see a psychiatrist who specialised in perinatal depression. She immediately took me off the second drug. A few days later I started on a different class of antidepressant and I felt extraordinarily calm.

I believe that the medication worked in the end. I did improve. Was it a placebo? Was it the sleep that this sedating drug gave me? I don't know, but I did get better.

I don't think I was well enough for counselling in the beginning, and by the time I was, our circumstances had improved so much. I had family and domestic help and I just went from strength to strength. The combination of the right drug, and some pretty serious hands on home help were what pulled me out of it.

I have learned that it is really important to pay attention to your feelings. I am stronger, more honest with myself and, next time, will act to put things right much sooner. I am learning to listen both to myself and to those around me.

My GP and child health nurse were straight onto it and had me on antidepressants within five weeks of my third child being born. I was too sick to resist being diagnosed. I just wanted someone to save me and that is what happened, fortunately.

My GP and child health nurse and psychologist were very caring and understanding but it took three goes to get the right psychiatrist. This was damaging as I was heavily medicated and it wasn't helping. Thank god for my psychiatrist now, she understands and is keen to wean me slowly off medication. I accept that I will need some meds for a long time.

Prozac was wrong for me and unfortunately it took a very high dosage for this to become obvious. On 80mg I went into a 'mixed state' thus showing signs of bipolar as far as the psychiatrist was concerned. I was in a very vulnerable position, powerless and at the mercy of professionals. Fortunately a change in medication at my request sorted this 'mixed state' out and Lexepro was introduced. Thank god it worked.

In hospital, I was very sick and so spent much of the time initially in my room. The nurses were great, talking with them brought me out of my shell. I was able to spend more time with my baby and had the opportunity to connect with other women, some of whom I still see. I also became very creative during my five-week stay and did several paintings out in the courtyard.

At that time, I was terrified. I couldn't see at the time just how I was going to become well enough to care for my baby and go home to my other two children who were missing me dearly. I felt like I had failed as a mother and partner.

I saw a psychologist for three years; she was very practical and helped me to sort through issues that had been unresolved for years. I was part of a postnatal depression support group, it was nice to relate to others.

What helped me the most was an extremely exceptional, supportive, loving husband who had an unwavering faith that I would get well.

I was the uptight, type A, high achieving, goal driven control freak. I lived my life according to the plans I made — until at the age of 31 I found myself unexpectedly ten-weeks' pregnant. After the initial shock, I planned: a herbal pregnancy, a herbal birth at the birth centre, midwife care, and to become a breastfeeding goddess.

The reality was threatened miscarriage, preeclampsia, obstetric involvement, hospital admission at 32 weeks, significant surveillance, eventual induction, complicated labour, extraordinary interventions by a variety of specialists, 24hrs later forceps delivery... and then the baby refused to breastfeed.

No-one, friend, relative or professional actually asked me how I was feeling. For the first time in my life I had failed at everything. At my six-week check up I tried to articulate to the obstetrician that things were not how I imagined and that I was trying to deal with repetitive intrusive thoughts. All he was interested in was whether we had managed to have sex again. We had, and in fact, I was to find out I was pregnant again just a few weeks later.

My anxiety began when my first baby was a couple of months old and that line appeared on that stick. My husband was so excited, I wept and told him that I couldn't go through the baby thing again. I spoke to the obstetrician but he didn't 'hear'.

I couldn't tell anyone else I was pregnant. The ECHC nurse was obsessed with the weight of the baby, the fact I was not breastfeeding, and told me that my son was fat and when he went to school he would be the fat boy in the playground and would have no friends. I decided to water down the formula. We never had a conversation about how I was getting on.

I finally went and had my first visit with the obstetrician at 22 weeks who checked all things physical and sent me on my way.

I had a lot of friends and family around and I was back at work. But I felt totally isolated. I would lie in bed at night silently weeping, feeling like this alien had invaded my body and was destroying my life and I had completely lost control. I was, however, a highly functioning, yet out of control woman and no one knew how I was really feeling. Denial can be very protective.

*This story is so open to judgement: pull yourself together —
we all have issues — stop being so self absorbed and get over
yourself — you have so many things to be thankful for: financial
security, relationships, career... the list is endless. I know there are
health professionals who see it this way.*

*The problem was that I was actually developing a mental
health problem. The anxiety was quite overwhelming and I was
emotionally very fragile. I felt raw and brittle, enveloped in
blackness and could see no way forward. Each day was a dark
and turbulent 'groundhog' day.*

*All the parenting books and magazines were full of the joys of
motherhood. My response was that I must be a bad mother and
so I did not want to share my dark thoughts with any of my
friends. I did not want them to judge me and I did not want
my babies scrutinised for signs of maladjustment. I put all my
emotional effort into appearing 'normal'.*

*I didn't realise I had a problem that could be worked through.
But if any of the health professionals had asked the right
questions I would have shared.*

*My main issue began as an adjustment disorder, coupled with a
posttraumatic stress disorder. The development into problems far
more complex could have been ameliorated by some professional
support. Adjustment disorders relating to parenthood are
common — many couples need help managing their expectations.
But hindsight is a very beautiful thing.*

*So my train wreck life just kept hurtling on. I did manage the
herbal birth experience for baby number two, with the midwife
and the birth centre. The amazing endorphin high dropped to
an amazing low literally as the placenta was delivered. I wept
and not from joy. I refused to share our 'happy news' with the
relatives and friends my husband was ringing. I begged him to*

stay with me but he left. I kept crying and no midwife came to talk to me.

No one asked how I felt now that I had two babies. Breastfeeding attempts resulted in cracked, bloody then pussy nipples and full blown mastitis all by day four. Following four weeks of expressing, the lactation consultant told me to stop, having completely destroyed my nipples which were never to recover.

My home life was surreal. This new baby was very unsettled, crying constantly, sleeping intermittently and I couldn't think clearly. He would spend 40 minutes uncomfortably consuming the milk I had spent an hour or more expressing, only to vomit it all back up 10 minutes later. Soul destroying.

Eventually I spoke to the ECHC nurse who informed me that my baby was allergic to milk. She never asked me how I was feeling. How I was coping with two babies under the age of one. Was I getting sleep, or help?

My diagnosis came by chance — a random conversation my husband had with a colleague. My husband was the only one who saw beyond the public facade. He saw the uncontrollable mood swings, the anger, the grief, the tears, the sitting on the floor and rocking, banging my head against the wall, the agitation, the scratching. But even he didn't know about the black, intrusive and disordered thoughts.

I was admitted to a psychiatric unit where I spent four quite strange weeks. While the diagnosis gave me great relief — there is a name for this madness — the subsequent discussions around plans for my care left me feeling quite disempowered. Everyone else was making decisions on my behalf without even bothering to ask me how I felt about this.

I hated being in that psychiatric hospital even though I knew I couldn't cope at home. I would sit alone staring out my bedroom window contemplating a quick jump. These suicidal thoughts continued for some months although I never told anyone. I was too scared to articulate how I was really feeling.

I spent many hours with a psychiatrist, but what I really needed was practical help, not psychoanalysis. I was pathologised rather than counselled.

I started to get better once a professional started working with where I was in my life. Many frontline health professionals feel underqualified when dealing with an anxious or depressed patient and find comfort in the ability to prescribe a drug — while drugs can be important, it is often far better to start with a referral for counselling.

My recovery journey was excruciating for everyone. It involved antidepressants, long-term cognitive behavioural therapy (CBT) and a lot of hard work and determination with the help of a psychologist — my salvation. She treated my husband and me together as a couple. The issue was not simply mine alone, and he was relieved because at last he was being included. Someone was listening to him.

I think the media does new mothers a disservice, bombarding us with celebrity motherhood pictures of Angelina or our Nicole managing beautifully. I think a good dose of Brittany would do a lot for the fragile self esteem of new mothers.

Our motherhood sisters also need to have a good look at themselves. In our competitive world we need to develop some generosity of spirit and offer some compassion. Perinatal mood disorders are real and debilitating — their impact is felt widely. My life was nearly destroyed by this illness.

Mothers who are struggling should not simply be pathologised, they need support and understanding. Hormones, chemicals, stress or personality — there are many factors impacting on the lives of new mothers: that bio-psycho-social model.

A bit of humanity can go a long way. We've all had horrible feelings at some time during our mothering experiences. We all know the value of a friend who will listen. One of the unexpected but interesting outcomes from an antenatal screening program recently piloted was the patients' expression of how they enjoyed being listened to by the midwives.

I can write this today because I eventually got better. But I don't believe that would have happened if I was not lucky enough to receive the professional help that I did.

Our personal experiences have influenced our journey in life — the turmoil and grief now behind us — my husband and I can now talk about it. We are a well-educated and well-connected couple yet perinatal anxiety and depression nearly destroyed our lives: how then must it impact on others without the resources we had?

I saw my GP several months ago and told her I felt like I was not coping. She wrote me out a mental health care plans with referrals to see a counsellor/psychologist. I haven't found there to be much support for postnatal depression so I've had to really try to help myself, which is hard some days. I've tried to get back into exercise because I know from past experience that cardio exercise can really help my mood because of the endorphins.

I've had depression for about 15 years. With my second pregnancy it got a lot worse in the last three months and I had a lot of anxiety attacks. I was already on Zoloft, so my dosage was increased to combat the increased depression. I also started seeing a counsellor, referred by Tresillian. She is fantastic and I have found it extremely helpful to speak to someone on a regular basis, especially someone with experience with new mums. The medication was, and is, helpful, but regular visits to a counsellor and exercise are also essential for me.

❧

I'm not depressed, I'm just very tired... at least that's what I was thinking and saying. I definitely suffered a lot of anxiety while I was pregnant. We sold our house and moved when I was 32 weeks, which was really stressful. The twins were born three weeks later, which I feel was due to the stress of selling and moving etc. Whether this anxiety contributed or not, I am unsure. Maybe it indicated a predisposition to depression.

I didn't feel ready to give birth. I felt disorganised and unprepared. My husband was retrenched when the twins were two weeks old, so there was financial pressure as well. Luckily we had just sold a house and we were able to live off our savings while my husband looked for work.

Also, the pressure I placed on myself increased after they turned one and started walking and running. With one of the twins having allergies, I was very concerned when she was in the care of her grandparents or at day care, and I hardly took any time for myself. They were only in care half a day a week after they were 18 months old.

When I was really depressed, I felt alone, I felt misunderstood. I felt repressed and I felt I could tell no one. I felt everything I did was wrong. I was extremely hard on myself and berated myself for not coping. I was tired, then I was angry, but mostly I was empty. I had given so much of myself away and I had nothing left. I felt very guilty.

My twins were born five weeks premmie, but were well, and only spent five days in special care before they were with me. I started struggling with looking after them by six weeks, and had a sleep specialist come to our house at eight weeks. Around the same time I discovered one of the girls had food allergies and could only be breastfed.

I felt like a freak at the mothers' group I was in. They all had perfect singleton babies and all my twins did was cry. So I stayed home a lot, and juggled feeding them separately, their opposite sleeping routines, and trying to look after myself. We went to a Tresillian at five months and 'failed'. I wasn't enjoying myself, my twins or my life.

'I'm not depressed, I'm just very, very tired' was the response I gave my early childhood nurse on numerous occasions. The fact that she never ended up referring me to the clinic, and did home visits until my twins were 15 months old should have clued me in to the fact that she was a little worried about me. I would talk to her about feeling extremely tired, how if one baby wasn't screaming then the other one was, and how I struggled getting them to settle and sleep at the same time.

Then there were the breastfeeding issues, which included three bouts of mastitis, a lack of supply by the end of the day, the fact that I had a poor feeder so had to feed them individually, which meant twice as long feeding, and then I had to listen to the other baby cry.

Then I found out that one of my babies was allergic to dairy and egg, so I didn't even have a choice about breastfeeding, and I had to avoid eating dairy and egg myself until I stopped breastfeeding at 14 months.

But I wasn't depressed! There were lots of other people out there worse off than me. I just found it hard work looking after my girls, and that, coupled with being overtired and hormonal, meant that the world wasn't the happy place it used to be. But surely anyone in these circumstances would be feeling the same, wouldn't they? Well, apparently not!!

I know that on the days I had more than five hours sleep I felt a bit better, but I really wasn't enjoying being a twin mum. I felt that nobody's babies cried as loudly or as long as mine did. No other mums I met seemed to have a baby with such bad colic and gastric problems.

Other mums looked liked they were coping, cooing over their bundles of joy. Why was it that I felt like I wasn't? But I had to cope. I had no choice. No one else was going to look after my babies. Even if I felt like I wasn't doing a very good job.

So I ploughed on, trying to be the perfect parent. I tried to juggle the very different needs of two little, always changing babies, while still being a wife, a homemaker and a business partner. I had no time for me, and even if I did, I wouldn't have known what to do with it.

There was always a very valid reason why I was having a bad day. Why I was crying again, and why I often didn't like my twins very much. I never, ever thought that I could be depressed. That was something that happened to other people. I was a strong and competent woman, and had worked for myself for ten years and accomplished things. I was not a victim, and I 'should' be enjoying my babies. Other mums seemed to be enjoying theirs. I had moments when I did, but overall, I can honestly say that nurturing two babies through their first 18 months was not a pleasure.

So I started doing things that were meant to make me feel better. I got out and about, met other twin mums, and became a zone representative for the club, exercised, ate well, but still I collapsed in a heap at 7pm.

In the end I was crying every other day, I was waking at 4am and not getting back to sleep, I would shout at the kids, and the one or two glasses of wine every night were all contributing factors in me finally wondering if perhaps, just maybe, there could be a small possibility that I might be depressed. I was physically and emotionally exhausted.

So, when my twins were 19 months old, I finally went to the doctor. 'Postnatal depression' she said. 'You've probably had it since your twins were born. It's just a temporary chemical imbalance in your brain, so let's fix it.'

I took me a week to decide how I was going to deal with it. Would I go on medication? Would I just get counselling, or would I do both? I decided to do both, and after just one week I felt a lot better. My anxiety levels dropped dramatically, and I was a lot calmer. As a result my girls were calmer.

After a month or so, I felt like a different person. I was feeling truly happier. Something I had not felt in a long time. I used to feel guilty, and think that I was a never a 'good enough' mother, but now I know that 'good enough' is great, and anything above that is a bonus. I have taken the pressure off myself, and more importantly off my girls.

The best thing about acknowledging my depression was that after I was feeling better I realised that I really was in love with my girls. Now I feel connected to them, an extraordinary bond. I can marvel in the joy that is them. They are unique and special and they have taught me so many things about myself. It doesn't have to be all hard work.

Motherhood had been a difficult journey for me, but now it is a journey I am enjoying very much. That is the difference. We still have hard days, but overall it's so much easier, and I am thankful that I finally sought help.

Unfortunately, I felt there was a stigma attached to depression. It was a while before I told people about it. I was embarrassed and didn't want to be judged. Now I don't mind who knows. I am not depressed any more but I know how hard living with it can be. If you are feeling down please talk to someone, a friend, your husband, your doctor. You never know. It just might help.

I'm currently seven months pregnant, and have had a bit of a rough ride so far. I have a diagnosis of bipolar disorder, so this was never going to be easy, but what I've found really difficult is the lack of information about depression in the prenatal period. Everyone seems to have heard of postnatal depression, but many people found it hard to understand that I'd been diagnosed with antenatal depression during the 1st trimester.

My case turned out to be all about withdrawal from medication, awful morning sickness and other life events... and has now 'resolved' — but I'm sure I can't be the only person to have gone through a period like that early on!

Plus, being told that you're 'at risk' of postnatal depression (and postpartum psychosis!) is really scary. I guess that's the downside of doing screenings early on.

I don't remember much other than being told 'don't worry too much'. An obstetrician also suggested to me that the reason my morning sickness was so severe was probably because I was too anxious, and that I needed to work on 'being at peace with the world'. I do recall one psychiatrist telling me I should read about it, because knowing the worst case scenario would help... but not really being able to suggest anything much for me to read except a very simple brochure — I think it was from beyondblue.

I'd say that seeing my psychologist has been a big factor in resolving the antenatal depression. I need to be reminded that I have dealt with depression many times before, and that I have learned lots of different strategies to cope. It was also nice to have someone who knew all of my history.

It took a lot of time. I had to slow down and concentrate on basic day-to-day tasks, rather than trying to do everything. I had to let go of all my ideas about things being 'perfect' — I was initially very susceptible to all those images in the media of perfectly-dressed babies and mums, and having the beautiful nursery... and the lovely ideas people gave me about how I should be keeping a journal or writing letters to the baby, or knitting, or... and all the fuss about whether to be a stay at home mum or to put my child in childcare, to breast or bottle feed, to use cloth or disposable nappies... etc.

In the end, what my baby needs is none of that stuff! Primarily my baby needs me to be well enough to care for him or her, to be loved, fed, and put to bed somewhere safe and comfortable. The baby won't know what colour everything is, or what brand it is, or any of that stuff! It took me a long time to realise that!

And I am not an island. Right now the baby gets everything it needs from me, but when it's born there are other people who will help out — I don't have to do everything!

What I have found really tricky is that the professionals I expected would look after me weren't willing to, given the risks associated with the drugs and my bipolar diagnosis. It has been intensely frustrating to go from GP to obstetrician, back to GP, to psychiatrist, back to GP, then to a new psychiatrist... with no one willing to make a decision about whether I should or shouldn't be on medication! I have felt lost, and alone, and really scared.

Occasionally, I have been asked if I have had thoughts about not keeping the baby... that makes me feel awful, and completely misunderstood.

I recently read a very good book: Understanding your moods when you're expecting *by Lucy Peryear. It was really helpful. It gave me a sense that some mood instability is normal, and not necessarily the red flags of bipolar disorder or anxiety or depression.*

I'm also really enjoying Attack of the Fifty Foot Hormones *by Emma Tom. This book is honest about pregnancy not being a totally wonderful experience, and about hormones making you tired/tearful etc.*

My obstetrician and psychiatrist are planning to keep me in the maternity ward for longer than a normal stay — probably a week. They don't want me going home until they're sure that I've recovered from the birth, and have feeding worked out.

My husband is trying to get a few weeks off work when the baby comes, so he can be at home with me, so I won't be isolated while I'm getting used to having a baby. I also have some friends lined up to help out, and have pre-warned them that 'help' could mean talking me out of irrational thoughts, housework, cooking, keeping me company, holding the baby... the idea being that I don't want to get too overwhelmed or stressed out.

I've also talked to my husband about limiting how much contact I have with people who are likely to annoy me or stress me out by criticising me for not dressing the baby warmly enough or having my house clean, etc.

I've stopped work already, which is giving me time to learn what it's like to be at home all day long. It has also given me a chance to build relationships and just hang out with other mums I know.

I felt that if I worked 'until the first contraction' that I would be very stressed about not having things ready, and also that I would find it really hard to adjust to the world of not being at work.

My psychiatrist has said he'll continue to monitor me after the birth, and for the next couple of years. It's not really worth me going back to someone who isn't willing or able to handle pregnancy and motherhood. If there is to be a sibling in a few years, it will be better for me in terms of planning, medication and treatment decisions. I know I'll appreciate the continuity.

My psychologist is willing to let me decide what I want to do at the moment. So for now I'm seeing her fortnightly, and we're talking a lot about what will happen with the birth/baby etc.

I think my advice to someone in my situation would be to fight until you find professionals who take your concerns seriously, AND actually talk to you! I eventually found the right people.

Also, I would say don't be afraid to go straight to the top — seeing a psychiatrist who specialised in perinatal mood disorders seemed like a big step, but it certainly helped. It means I'm going to be giving birth at a tertiary hospital, rather than my local, but I think it's worth it to be looked after well!

Actually, I think women with mood disorders should really ask more questions of the doctors who prescribe them medications, whether they're pregnant or not! I've since found out from my current psychiatrist who specialises in perinatal mood disorders that I could have started out years ago with medications that are considered much safer for women of child-bearing age, which would have saved me a lot of stress when I did become unexpectedly pregnant. Unfortunately I was a bit of a victim of 'one size fits all' prescribing, and didn't think to ask questions.

We were given a small handbook and postnatal depression was sort of talked about at the birthing classes but not in great detail. I just thought I would cope — it would be easy — like everything I have done in life. I am personality Type A, have worked fulltime my whole adult life and don't know babies etc! I thought it would be easy! Little did I know…

Parenthood is a huge life change that is not something that someone can describe to you. I was shocked by how life was with a baby. I didn't have a clue, didn't know what to do. It was horrible. I couldn't shut my thoughts down and I couldn't sleep so it was a cycle between anxiety and sleep deprivation.

I was very anxious, which made me feel depressed: Why wasn't I coping? Was I a bad mother? Why couldn't I breastfeed? Was what I was doing ok? Was that person judging me? All I felt was anxiety and depression — I am not naturally a depressed person so this was really hard to deal with.

I came home early as I had what the hospital deemed an easy birth. In hindsight, I felt very overwhelmed and wanted to be in my own environment. I felt judged by the midwives and I couldn't get the breastfeeding. I was also tired and I thought that I would be better at home. Looking back it was the start of postnatal depression. I am a very strong person by nature so it was strange to feel so out of my depth.

Joining the postnatal depression group was the best experience. I felt so normal and so unjudged. We would meet every Friday from 10am–12pm. We discussed everything — it was free and flowing, we had art therapy, tea, cake and a shoulder to cry on. I believe this made the experience a positive one for me and it was easier for me to heal.

I also saw a private counsellor outside of this group to further discuss my feelings and realised what I was feeling was normal.

I also did a lot of reading on the subject and this made it a better experience for me. I never saw it as negative.

My advice to other people:
- *get help early and don't be afraid of the journey — keep talking and don't be afraid*
- *read, read, read and watch and learn, be honest and open.*

Improvements I'd like to see:
- *I think that all mothers post birth should have a trained counsellor come to their house and assess their emotional head space, as well as the maternal health nurse. I don't think reviewing a paper-based test is the best way to assess perinatal depression.*
- *Seeing someone during the pregnancy who could have talked to me more about my feelings would have been really helpful.*
- *There should be much more education at the birth classes, my suggestion is to get a counsellor in as part of those sessions to describe what perinatal depression looks like, etc so that partners can be aware of what they can do and what to look out for.*
- *Mums should have more time in hospital if required or wanted — you should be able to pay if you want to stay. If your baby is healthy you are kicked out before your breast milk is even in, having had very little sleep and then the whole thing snowballs.*

Having this experience has made me more appreciative of mothers, and of my husband and my beautiful son. Now I try to live in the moment and not try and control everything.

That is can happen to anyone — it knows no bounds. Depression is not a dirty word! Not talking about it is!

9
DADS AND DEPRESSION

The ultimate life-defining moment is becoming a father.

When my babies were little, their mother descended into a hell of postnatal depression. My wife ended up in hospital on medication. I was a lousy husband, yelling, critical, a complete failure as a husband, a father and a man. I live with the regret of the lost years of my marriage and my early relationship with my children.

I love my role as a father and I'm proud that my family made it.

Fatherhood matters. It's important.

WHAT ABOUT DAD?

Traditionally, pregnancy, childbirth and all things related, have been secret women's business. Much has happened in a generation. It was only the social revolution of the early 1970s that dragged men out of the pub and into the birthing room, some reluctantly, others with great enthusiasm. It has taken a single generation for men to move from the place where they were thanked for 'helping' if they managed to change a nappy, to the place they now inhabit, where many expect — and indeed want — to share all the responsibilities of fatherhood.

Once upon a time the father would leave the new mother and baby at home, returning to work safe in the knowledge that all was at peace in the world. Roles were clearly defined: fathers provided financial support while mothers became queens of domesticity. This is no longer necessarily the case, and many men struggle with their new role. Not only are they expected to be the hunter and gatherer, they must return at the end of the day and be the nurturer, and often cook, cleaner and babysitter.

While many fathers enjoy their new role it is not uncommon for some fathers to experience perinatal anxiety and depression too. It's estimated that around 10% of fathers will experience some form of anxiety and depression during this period.[1]

Visions of being a dad are often accompanied by enthusiasm and anticipation for what lies ahead. However, the reality of weeks of sleepless nights, a crying baby, a changing or even deteriorating relationship with your partner and having to head off to work each morning feeling exhausted can shatter the dream.

The problem is, of course, that if you are the family's provider, you have to keep working and be a diligent employee, and that is hard to do when you are also so tired.

The stress factors that influence a mother's state of mind will also be similar for a father. Difficulty sleeping, dealing with an unsettled baby, issues related to the labour and birth, and unmet expectations of fatherhood can be coupled with the demands of work and self-imposed pressures. Many men feel overwhelmed by their new sense of responsibility, both financial and emotional.

Anxiety and depression in fathers can manifest in two different ways

Perinatal anxiety and depression are not simply a woman's issue. Fathers' lives can also be significantly impacted during this time.

Firstly, and most obviously, men can suffer a reactive depression directly related to the way their partner may be feeling. Living with someone who is always 'down' can eventually bring the other person 'down'. In fact, anxiety and depression in mothers is the strongest predictor for anxiety and depression in fathers.

Secondly, men can also experience their own anxiety and depression during this time, quite independently of the way their partner may be feeling.

ADJUSTMENT TO FATHERHOOD

To be honest, I had no idea what to expect. It was many years since I had been in close contact with a newborn baby. I think like a lot of men, you tend to play a supportive role in this period — reassuring your wife that we'll be fine, the birth will be ok, we will manage — all that. Because you do so much talking up, you tend to mask out any uncertainties or worries you might feel.

The problem was that we had twins and a toddler when I would have been happy to just have one child.

The things I did not anticipate were the sheer exhaustion that quickly envelopes you. Having a newborn baby in the house is like living in a submarine: night and day no longer have any meaning. You just stagger through this four-hour cycle of feeding, sleeping, changing, and that is if things are going well and you have a four-hour cycle.

'*We are not going to let this baby alter our relationship*'... these are very common famous last words spoken by many a prospective father! Yet, becoming a father is actually the ultimate upheaval in any man's life and requires emotional adjustments to be made.

Many men are ill prepared for this. The obvious physical and emotional changes that impact on the mother during pregnancy can be a constant reminder to her that life is changing, but men are physically and often emotionally distant from this. While they may be excited about the prospect of impending fatherhood, this is often just a vague concept. Dads may not need to completely redefine their identity, but they may become overwhelmed by their sense of responsibility, and the physical and emotional changes occurring in their home that they simply had not anticipated.

It would have been hard not to feel some anxiety or depression having three kids under the age of two while juggling a small business, and then having to cope with my father's ill health as well.

Some reasons for feeling unsettled at this time:
- The pregnancy may have been unplanned. Even planned pregnancies can take some getting used to. Complications with the pregnancy can cause a lot of stress and anxiety.
- There may be financial pressures. Many couples seem to find themselves moving house or renovating at this time: activities which are inherently stressful in themselves.
- The birth may not have unfolded as anticipated. While men generally feel enriched by supporting their partner through the birth of their child, a percentage will find the experience confronting and distressing. They may feel alienated and unsure of their role even if the birth is straightforward, and especially so if there are complications.
- If there are problems — and particularly if there are emergencies during the labour and birth — fathers can feel completely out of place, forgotten, or in some instances a complete nuisance and totally in the way. Some fathers may

feel traumatised after a dramatic birth experience. It's very rare that fathers are given the opportunity to debrief if things have not gone as planned and this can create long term emotional problems.

- Fathers can feel excluded after the baby arrives. Health professionals focus on the new mum and baby as they help establish feeding and support the mother in learning to care for her baby. Even the language used by some health professionals can alienate fathers. The mother, of course, is also focused on her new baby.

WHERE EXACTLY DOES A FATHER FIT INTO THIS MATERNAL-CENTRED WORLD?

I think men are poorly trained for dealing with situations like the early weeks and months of being a dad. We are taught to be stoic, unemotional, not to talk about what we are really feeling. We feel we just have to cope, be reliable. If we are feeling anxious or upset or uncertain, we hide it.

It is a big shock for most of us, I think, especially if you have children reasonably late in life, so it is a long time since you have experienced living with a baby.

With the birth of a baby a couple has suddenly become a family. Many women feel so overwhelmed by the need to be everything to their baby that they feel they don't have any capacity left for their primary relationship. They will often feel exhausted, sleep-deprived and emotional, even if they are not suffering from anxiety or depression. Many men expect their relationship with their partner will just pick up again, and might become confused and even irritated when it does not.

I think I also failed to appreciate how exhausted my wife would be, and I was not expecting her to suffer depression or anything like that. Because I assumed she would be fine, that we would cope, that all would be well, it probably took me longer than it should have to recognise that something was wrong.

Some things to consider:

- For lots of mothers with new babies any thought of bed is accompanied by fantasies of sleep, not sex. Most women will have a major drop in libido after they've given birth, from which it can take months, even years, to recover. Intimacy is a major casualty when a third person joins the relationship. Many men are not prepared for this.
- New fathers may offer affection in the secret hope it might lead to sex. When they are rejected they may retreat, feeling hurt and rejected, and seriously frustrated in all senses of the word.
- Even understanding men with the best intentions can feel superfluous during the early weeks of fatherhood. They may not really know what their new role should be and fear criticism for doing the wrong thing. If their partner is breastfeeding they may even feel that they have been replaced as the main object of her affection. As the weeks unfold they may feel overcommitted: juggling work and family, while also experiencing possible stress over financial pressures.
- Most men are unlikely to chat about their feelings with their mates, and many would struggle to know where to go to seek help.

Fathers may feel pulled in different directions. While they'll feel the need to support their partner and new baby, they may also want to spend time with their mates. Many women may resent this.

For men, a lot of 'me time' takes place away from the family, and also takes a bit of time. You often let this slip, as you feel torn between work and family. This is understandable, but it can be a trap. If you are going to be much use to your wife and child, you need to look after yourself, and that means maintaining your exercise, eating sensibly, that sort of thing.

During this time, it's possible you may feel your partner does not appreciate the work that you are doing outside the home. You might feel that the stresses and responsibilities of your working life are overlooked and lost within this new baby dynamic. It is very easy for a father to feel that his partner has become so focused on herself and her baby that she has forgotten that the world outside the home can also be very stressful.

Many new parents are not prepared for how hard the first few months are with a new baby. Even wonderful relationships can experience moments of dysfunction during this time. If not recognised, the dysfunction can become significant very quickly and easily, as the father begins to feel irrelevant in this new dynamic created by the addition of one small, but demanding, human. A deteriorating relationship between parents can lead to a father finding excuses for staying away from a fractious home environment. This can induce feelings of guilt and resentment which can be played out in all sorts of negative ways.

Time and communication are the keys. However, when you live with a new baby, those commodities are in short supply. Being realistic and aware of these limitations is half the battle. Finding some time to be kind and understanding towards each other is the other half. If a new mother feels she can communicate with her partner, and feels supported and understood by him, she is less likely to develop anxiety and depression.[2] In turn, a new father is more likely to also have his needs understood.

Unrecognised anxiety and depression can lead to serious relationship dysfunction. Anecdotally there are many stories of divorced couples, who on reflection, will identify the beginning of the end of their relationship with the distress they experienced with the arrival of a new baby. Many people will look back to this time with regret, wishing that they had had the knowledge, insight and resources to seek help. Instead they struggled on, often acrimoniously, with a deteriorating relationship and thus missed some special moments of life with a new baby.

WE NEED TO FOCUS MORE ON FATHERHOOD

The transition to fatherhood and the adjustment issues men face are not widely discussed. The media does not dwell on fathers in the same way that it scrutinises motherhood. Antenatal classes focus on women, and do not necessarily provide an environment where men feel particularly comfortable. Women can seek postnatal care from a number of services including the Early Childhood Health Centre (ECHC) nurse, midwife, GP, even their obstetrician. In fact, men may be unintentionally marginalised by health services which are set up essentially to provide support for women. [3]

Men don't tend to seek medical advice unless they are experiencing acute physical illness, and they rarely seek professional advice about emotional issues. There are few options for men seeking information on their upcoming journey as a father (see the Resource Guide for some that are available). As a result, most men don't give this much thought. They approach fatherhood without insight or awareness of the demands it will place on them and how this will impact on their life.

Typically, men also don't tend to share their thoughts and feelings the way women do. They may have great mates and share fun times, but usually not personal feelings and stories. Nor should they feel pressured to do so if being deep and meaningful does not sit comfortably with them.

Relatively recently there have been a few attempts to introduce 'transition to parenthood' classes and some of these have included classes that focus on the father.[3] Classes that addressed the emotional changes that occur during early parenthood helped to raise awareness of these issues with prospective fathers. It was found, in turn, that the mothers' experiences were improved by their partners' awareness.

THE DIFFICULTIES OF CARING FOR AN ANXIOUS AND DEPRESSED PARTNER

Be aware of your mates who are new parents and help them out. Put out the garbage, give them a call, talk about how hard it is. Don't get deep and meaningful, that's not what blokes do. Just validate the feelings and then talk about rugby.

The twilight zone aspect of early parenthood is intensified if the mother becomes unwell. If the mother does become unwell there is an increased chance that the father will also suffer from anxiety and depression.[4] It can be a shock for many men when the woman they love becomes an alien, when the birth of a baby creates within their partner a completely different personality. In this situation, they may feel their partner has changed forever; the person they fell in love with has been replaced. These feelings can manifest as anger, which can be directed at their partner and also at others such as doctors and midwives, even relatives and friends.

Men can feel angry because they don't understand exactly what's going on with their partner. They may feel excluded from the care she is receiving and feel they are just expected to cope with it all. This was the case for the partner of one of the authors. He was actively excluded from the care his wife was receiving. The health professionals involved made it very clear his presence was not welcome; it was only the mother they were treating.

Men may also experience grief and loss that their dream of family life has been shattered by their partner's illness. They might feel exhausted and overwhelmed. Some might question the veracity of perinatal mood disorders and wonder why their partner just can't 'snap out of it'. Or they may feel that they just want to 'fix it'. Unfortunately, perinatal mood disorders can't just be 'fixed', which is difficult for many men to accept. The stigma associated with perinatal anxiety and depression often means that issues going on behind closed doors are not discussed with anyone else. Furthermore, many fathers have no idea where they can turn to for support.

WHAT DOES ANXIETY AND DEPRESSION FEEL LIKE FOR DADS?

One of the reasons why I actually feel my experience of postnatal depression was a blessing is that it forced me to face the fact that I had been depressed most of my life, certainly since I was in primary school. I had been aware of this in a way, but was half in denial. I handled my depression by avoiding commitment or situations which were stressful. It worked after a fashion, but you can't achieve a huge deal in life that way, and you certainly can't be a good dad and a good husband.

I felt drained most days, and at times angry and pissed off at the situation. I had a much shorter fuse.

It was a state of paralysis. I just felt unable to do anything. The smallest task, making a phone call, returning a book to the library, seemed overwhelming. I would find myself bursting into tears at the smallest problem. I was utterly exhausted. I would actually fall asleep while walking home from the train. I felt that there was nothing in my life except a long list of tasks I couldn't hope to complete. Ironically, because I lost weight, quite a few people complemented me on my appearance.

Research in this area is new and rather limited. There is not even a DSM-IV (see page 79) psychiatric classification for this condition. Thus, a lot more work needs to be done, looking at men and their responses to fatherhood. Research should also look at ways to best support fathers.

A common male response to these feelings is to just 'get on with it' and hopefully 'get over it'. Men are unlikely to share these emotions, believing they are the only ones experiencing them, and as a result they feel isolated and lonely, or even trapped. Men experiencing postnatal anxiety and depression may feel that their life is out of control. They may feel angry with the world and direct this towards anyone around them. This anger can be frightening and even shocking to some new dads who may never have experienced such extreme emotions before. Some men feel trapped and resentful; others feel completely hopeless and helpless. At this time it can become very easy to blame the partner.

It has been shown that many men seem very ill prepared for fatherhood.[5] While a struggling father can have a significant impact on his family there are limited father-specific services he can access for help.[3]

If this happens to you, you may feel life will never again return to normal. The sense of failure can be overwhelming: you may believe you have failed as a father and a husband. This can be coupled with an overwhelming feeling of disappointment that fatherhood has not lived up to expectations. It's important not to feel stuck. Babies grow and change and life moves on. Try and see that this time is just one small part of the journey that is fatherhood.

WHAT FACTORS CAN INFLUENCE A FATHER'S WELLBEING?

As with mothers, biological, psychological and social factors influence the father's wellbeing:

- There is a high chance if a mother is depressed a father may also be, as research suggests this appears to be the case in 50% of couples. Fathers have also been shown to experience anxiety and depression during the antenatal period.[3]
- If there is a personal or family history of anxiety and/or depression there may be at higher risk of perinatal depression. A history of alcohol or drug dependence also increases the risk.
- Some personality types are more predisposed to depression after the birth of a baby. Men who are anxious or worriers may particularly be at risk, as providing financial and emotional

support to their new family may feel like an overwhelming responsibility.

- If close relationships with family, and particularly a partner, are strained, a father may be more vulnerable to depression at this time.
- Becoming a father is a major life event. Other common changes during this time such as moving house or changing jobs should be recognised as stressful and can also have a significant impact on the wellbeing of the family.

WHEN DOES A DAD HAVE A PROBLEM?

Men suffering from anxiety and depression will complain of a variety of symptoms. You may feel that you have lost your sense of humour and that there is no fun left in life. In fact you can feel miserable most of the time. Coupled with this can be feelings of anxiety, even panic, along with difficulty sleeping.

When you're depressed, it's easy to find yourself becoming irritable over all sorts of minor issues. This irritation can rapidly deteriorate into anger, or manifest as stress, both at work or at home. Dealing with these emotional issues can include lashing out, withdrawing, or perhaps drinking more than usual amongst other things.

Symptoms experienced by men with postnatal anxiety and depression are similar to those experienced by women:

- tiredness, irritability, anxiety, anger and resentment
- loss of enjoyment in life
- loss of libido
- changes in appetite
- problems sleeping
- feelings of being overwhelmed, out of control and unable to cope
- engaging in risk-taking behaviour

- using alcohol or drugs to help ease the symptoms
- feeling isolated and disconnected from partner, friends or family
- withdrawing from all relationships
- using work as an excuse for lack of connectedness.

The Edinburgh Postnatal Depression Scale (EPDS) (see page 73) is a good starting point in assessing how a new father is travelling. Validated for use with women it is now more frequently being used for men. When used as a screening tool, a score of 12 or higher in the EPDS will indicate that the father is struggling and in need of support and follow up.

WHERE CAN FATHERS ACCESS HELP?

If you are a dad and feel you may be experiencing perinatal depression and anxiety it's vitally important for your family that you seek help. Depression is an illness, not a weakness. When both the mother and father are experiencing perinatal anxiety and depression it can impact on the development of the infant; a well father, however, can act as a buffer to ameliorate the impact of a mother suffering anxiety and depression.[3, 6]

There is help available for fathers, but it is limited as most services are still orientated towards helping mothers. There is a growing understanding in the community that fathers also need support and hopefully this will lead to a growth in male-oriented services.

Help for dads on the web (see also the Resource Guide)

Ngala, a provider of early parenting services in Western Australia, and *beyondblue* have produced a booklet called *Hey Dad. Fatherhood — First 12 Months,* which is available to download from the *beyondblue* website **www.beyondblue.org.au**.

PANDA also have a fact sheet, *Men and Postnatal Depression* which can be obtained from their website **www.panda.org.au**

Other Useful websites:

www.beerandbubs.com.au	Birth classes for dads
www.postpartummen.com	US site with quite good information
www.dadsclub.com.au	Australian site with lots of general information relevant for Dads

Some general ideas on seeking help:

- Contacting your GP is often a good starting point. You might find it easier to make an appointment for a physical check-up and in the course of the conversation mention how you are feeling. Remember GPs talk to patients every day about the way they are feeling, and there are GPs who have an excellent understanding of where men might be coming from. Some GPs offer counselling, others will offer referral options for counselling, for example to a psychologist or psychiatrist who specialises in postnatal anxiety and depression. Medicare rebates are now available for people accessing these services (see page 285). GPs are also able to prescribe medication if they feel it's appropriate.

- Attending counselling as a couple may also be beneficial. While you might prefer individual counselling, this gives you the opportunity to work through issues together and address the dynamics in the relationship. Counselling enables couples to better understand and appreciate each other. It provides a neutral and supportive setting for concerns and frustrations to be aired and for issues to be worked through in a positive way. Some support groups offer specific counselling services for fathers (see Resources Guide).

- The **PANDA** national helpline **1300 726 306** can provide information to assist men who are experiencing difficulties during this postnatal period. You can also contact this phone line to seek help if you are concerned about your partner.

WHAT CAN HELP A DAD FEEL BETTER?

I went to see a doctor, and when he asked, I said I was prepared to take the tablets. The first medication I took was reasonably effective.

All the symptoms and feelings were due to the difficult family situation. This would only improve as the children grew and when we managed to get more help eg with a nanny.

Tablets alone won't fix everything, of course. But my experience is that all the other stuff you have to do: find a counsellor, have those tough conversations with your wife and other members of your family, find a support group, tell your work that you need support and a more family-friendly schedule, drink less, get fitter — all these things become possible once you have found the right medication, because you feel stronger, more yourself.

While it may feel daunting, seek practical and emotional support from the people around you. This is not always easy to do especially for men who have often been encouraged to be 'stoic' and 'strong'. You may find support from your partner, family, friends, or even work colleagues, and this will depend on the relationships you have and the trust you feel you can place in these individuals.

Try to find some time for yourself and for activities you enjoy. Participating in sport and exercise can help lift your mood. This can require effort and organisation but it's very important and always worthwhile. A friend might be able to babysit for a few hours to enable you and your partner to go for a walk together, or have a meal out. Try to keep up with your mates even if it is not as often as before. Just spending some time with people you enjoy can be positive.

Many health professionals have a growing awareness of the difficulties faced by fathers. While obstetricians, midwives clinics and early childhood centres may be the domain for mothers there are a growing number of GPs who are becoming more sensitive to the unique circumstances in which a struggling father may find himself.

However, there is as yet no gender specific screening tool, and in most cases fathers are simply the partner of their patient. Our current health system is not particularly user friendly for fathers. Unless the father feels comfortable in accessing health services it is difficult to help him.

It is important to remember that perinatal anxiety and depression is not a life sentence. Through receiving appropriate help and support the symptoms will be reduced and you will start to feel better. You will eventually be able to find there is so much to enjoy in being a father.

10
SPECIAL CASES

Pregnancy and childbirth can sometimes create particular challenges that may tip a woman into anxiety and depression, or make her recovery from a perinatal mood disorder a little bit more complicated.

TWINS OR MULTIPLE BIRTHS

Physically I sailed through the pregnancy and birth experience, mentally I struggled enormously to come to terms with the fact I was having twins.

I wasn't prepared for the lack of sleep. That was a shock to the system! My second was a dream baby. I was a lot more in control... then I had twins.

We should have left a bigger gap between the first child and the twins. But we didn't know we were going to have twins.

It was as tough as I thought it was going to be. Limiting, feeling isolated and that most people around me just 'didn't get it'.

The reaction couples have when they find out they are expecting twins can range from distress to delight. For couples with kids already at home, who decide to have one more to finish their family, the discovery that that one is actually two (or more) can come as quite a shock. For families experiencing financial difficulties or an unplanned pregnancy it may even be an unpleasant shock. On the other hand, first-time parents may be thrilled that a single pregnancy will produce a ready-made family, especially if the twins were conceived by assisted reproductive technology such as in vitro fertilisation.

However, even those approaching a twin pregnancy with stars in their eyes may eventually get a reality check. Twin pregnancy can be an anxious time. Women pregnant with multiples are at higher risk of medical complications, such as diabetes or preeclampsia, and some may even need to be admitted to hospital for long periods of bed rest. Occasionally, and very distressingly, there may even be the loss of one baby. Multiple pregnancies are more likely to be associated with premature delivery and neonatal intensive care admission, emotionally stressful situations in themselves (see below).

Even if they are born healthy and hearty, twins are twice as much work: two babies to feed (especially challenging if you're hoping to breastfeed), two babies to bathe and change, and two babies who will cry and not want to sleep at the same time. Sleep deprivation can become overwhelming. Simply getting out of the house with twins is much harder too, increasing the likelihood of social isolation. Multiple births can be the cause of stress and anxiety for fathers as well and this may result in marital tension.[1]

We used to recommend parenthood to all of our friends who had not yet started having babies. Then our twins came along and changed everything.

I can't quite recall feeling truly dreadful with my first baby. I do remember how easy things were and feeling like we could have more babies. It wasn't until the twins were born that I

*frequently felt dreadful. I think how bad you feel has a lot to
do with how much sleep and rest you're getting.*

*The small daily lows, the witching hours that occurred daily
with the twins from around one month to around six months,
were just terrible. One of the twins needed to be constantly
carried, or he'd be screaming. I strapped my kids on to my
back and front in carriers and walked around the house or the
courtyard every evening waiting for my husband to get home.*

*When the twins started to get very mobile at around 16
months, I became house bound unless I had someone else to
help me with the kids. Going anywhere on my own became
dangerous and exhausting, as the twins would not stay happy
in the pram.*

*Whilst I was depressed, I kept thinking: I have nothing to
complain about, I have a home, I have a supportive husband, I
have three beautiful children... mothers in the 1700s and 1800s
had it a lot tougher than I did... Why can't I deal with this?
Why can't I do the little bit I have to do, compared with those
amazing pioneering women that had it a thousand times harder
than me? I couldn't stop myself thinking about that all the
time. Of course that didn't help me acknowledge the fact that I
had a problem. I kept saying, 'Stupid woman — get it together',
because you think: I have nothing to complain about.*

A recent American study assessed the relationship between
multiple births and depressive symptoms in 8000 mothers, nine
months after delivery. They found moderate to severe depression
in 19% of mothers of multiple births, compared with 16% of
mothers of singletons. When the researchers took into consideration
demographic and socioeconomic factors, they found that mothers
experiencing multiple births were 40% more likely to have depressive
symptoms than mothers of singletons.[1] Mothers of multiples also
had a higher risk of giving birth to premature babies, and having

caesareans or otherwise complicated labours. Interestingly, mothers of multiples were no more likely to have mental health problems than mothers of singletons *before* delivery, indicating that it was the birth and its aftermath — the demands of looking after two or more babies — that lead to depression.

What can we take away from this study? If you are expecting or have delivered twins, you are clearly at increased risk of a perinatal mood disorder.

Health professionals, from your obstetrician to your GP and child and family health nurse, should be keeping a closer than normal eye on your mental health. However, even if you're being carefully watched, anxiety and depression may still arise. Months of sleep deprivation, social isolation and relentless demands on your time can wear even the hardiest soul down.

> *I did look up postnatal depression symptoms and not all of them were me. I didn't have problems sleeping. I was dead to the world but tired all the time... I was shouting at my older son. Almost anything would set me off, the slightest thing. My poor boy, he really copped it.*

> *I got to the doctor quite late. I should have gone much earlier. There were times when I said, 'Right I'm going to do it,' then I kept telling myself, 'No you're imagining things'. And I do like to think of myself as an intelligent woman but when it came to depression, I did feel that stigma, and I did feel like 'oh my God, no, it can't be me, it can't happen to me'.*

It may seem the hardest thing in the world to admit you're struggling, but please don't feel ashamed or guilty. With the right sort of treatment, support from loved ones and time you can recover from anxiety and depression.

It's natural that you — and your partner — will need more support than the parents of a single baby, so accept all reasonable offers of help and cut yourself some slack about the housework. The best gifts you can probably give yourself at this time are sleep, rest and some positive couple time.

> *I knew it would be hard so I made tough love decisions early on to try and make it easier. I didn't breastfeed and got a nanny by the time the boys were four months old to make going back to work easier.*

> **My GP said look, as you're a borderline case I would probably not give you medication, but I know your situation, I know you don't have any babysitters and I know you can't go to see a counsellor on a regular basis, which is what I would suggest normally, so I will give you some medication and we'll see how it goes. And I have to say it has helped me enormously. I know I have issues and I know I have to talk to a counsellor at some stage and once the children are starting school I will address that.** *

> *I started to unravel when the twins were six to nine months; there was lots of stress... Then I started shouting and my dad was a shouter and I promised myself I wouldn't do that... I spoke to my aunt about it and she actually picked it first. She said, 'This doesn't sound like you, and you're the first to say you don't like how you're dealing with your children. Do you think there might be something wrong?'... But it took me almost another year to get help.*

Look out for support groups for families with twins or other multiples. One place to start is the Australian Multiple Birth Association (AMBA) www.amba.org.au. Getting in contact with other mothers with twins and triplets — your new 'tribe' — can make you feel much less alone. These mothers know only too well what you're going through.

*The mother quoted above used medication to manage her symptoms, to good effect. The authors of this book are not endorsing the use of medication in lieu of other treatments; talking therapies are still recommended first-line for mild to moderate depression. However, this woman's stories do raise an important point: for mums of multiples even getting to a counselling session can prove a huge logistical challenge.

In recognition of the extra physical and emotional demands multiple births place on families, *beyondblue* have produced a special version of their booklet, *Emotional health during pregnancy and early parenthood for parents of multiple birth children*. If you haven't already done so we'd strongly recommend you get hold of a copy.

Visit **www.beyondblue.org.au** or call **1300 22 4636.**

BABIES WITH HEALTH CHALLENGES OR SPECIAL NEEDS

I suffered a lot of anxiety, and really it was never treated. My daughter was born two months premature and the doctors quickly noticed how floppy she was and did all sorts of tests. She was diagnosed with Prader-Willi Syndrome, a very rare disorder. I was a mess the day after the diagnosis; the nursing staff were wonderful though and very warm. But my husband was having a hard time and asked if there was a psychologist at the hospital but they didn't have one.

When my little girl was born, she was seven weeks premmie and born by emergency section. I was a wreck. I felt isolated, as if no-one understood. I hadn't slept for days and I was crying, sobbing, so shaken. I had been yelling at my husband: 'Stop telling people mother and baby are doing well. MOTHER AND BABY ARE NOT DOING WELL.' I couldn't understand why I was so out of control.

Then I got pregnant with my little boy and he came early too, so I had two premmie babies, 15 months apart and my little boy had to stay in hospital for weeks; he was floppy and unresponsive. It turned out to be cerebellar ataxia, we found out much later… it's on the cerebral palsy spectrum.

*We were given the diagnosis and then just sent off with no
follow up... We needed counselling, we needed to talk through
the diagnosis and what it meant.*

When most women arrive at the hospital to give birth they assume
they'll be leaving a few days later with a healthy infant in the
baby capsule. Sometimes, however, babies are born with extra
health challenges: prematurity, low birth-weight, developmental
disabilities and so on. This can come as a huge and unexpected
blow to the parents. If the baby is admitted to a neonatal intensive
care unit, there will also be anxious days and sleepless nights and
very little chance to bond.

*At 3am one night, the midwife said to me: 'You are grieving, it's
normal...' I was grieving, grieving the loss of the pregnancy, the
birth I had hoped for. And I had this tiny premmie baby with
tubes all over her. It was not the first child experience anyone
would hope for. I wasn't ready and she wasn't ready.*

If your baby has being diagnosed with a disability things may
seem little better even after you've returned home. Your child will
have extra hurdles to overcome throughout their life and thus so
will you. It's natural to go through a grieving process at this time.

Two of the authors of this book are mothers of special needs
children (in our case, an autism spectrum disorder). Although
neither of us knew anything was amiss at the time of our children's
births, we know only too well the pain and guilt that accompanies
a disability diagnosis. It is typical for the mother to ask, 'What
did I do wrong during my pregnancy to cause this?' even if health
professionals assure her she is in no way to blame. It's not surprising
that many mothers (and fathers) succumb to perinatal anxiety and
depression during this time.

A group of Canadian researchers recently looked at the research
conducted around preterm (<38 weeks' gestation) and low birth
weight (<2.5 kg) babies and found that mothers of preterm babies
were at higher risk of depression than mothers of full-term infants.

This was especially true for mothers of very low birth weight babies (<33 weeks gestation and <1.5kg), who were still more depressed than other mothers at one year post birth — possibly because these very small babies would have had a longer stay in hospital, and potentially permanent disabilities as a consequence of their prematurity.[2]

Anxiety disorders, such as posttraumatic stress disorder can also be a consequence of premature birth.[3]

> *I became very anxious about the future, about not knowing what it would be like. No-one could tell me what would happen. My daughter was on oxygen when we got home from hospital and I had to learn CPR in case she stopped breathing. She was tube fed; she had a breathing monitor at night. I would be up all night worrying about everything. Looking back, I can see this was all terrible, terrible anxiety.*

> **I didn't feel as if I was in my own skin, at times I was completely out of control. One day I would be fine, baking and organising, next day I'd absolutely lose it, overreacting, going ballistic... I felt like everyone was making huge demands constantly and I was failing because I couldn't fulfil them all. I had this erupting monster inside me.**

Just as it is for parents of multiples, parents of 'premmies' and children with disabilities need extra, individualised support. It's a really good idea to seek out parents in a similar situation, people who can provide both practical advice and a sympathetic ear.

AustPrem is one such organisation: **www.austprem.org.au.** It hosts chat groups where you can connect with other mums and dads who understand the unique challenges of being parents of prems.

STILLBIRTH, MISCARRIAGE AND NEONATAL DEATH

It's a reality that no parent ever wishes to face, but tragically some will. According to the Australian Institute of Health and Welfare about 1 in 100 Australian babies will be lost to stillbirth — death of a baby *in utero* prior to or during birth — or neonatal death (infant death within 28 days of birth) each year.[4] Many more women will miscarry before their baby reaches 20 weeks' gestation.

After a baby is lost, the mother's body will recognise that she is no longer pregnant. Her 'pregnancy hormones' will drop just as if she'd delivered a healthy baby, with sometimes distressing consequences, such as 'the milk coming in' when there is no baby to feed.

For both miscarriage and stillbirth, the highest risk of depression appears to be within six months of pregnancy loss, with childless women especially vulnerable after miscarriage.[3] Of course, in the aftermath of miscarriage, stillbirth or early infant death, the point where grief ends and depression starts will be hazy, although some experts have suggested that if grief and anxiety are still undiminished six to nine months after stillbirth then clinical depression should be suspected.[5] What is clear is that parents will need support and counselling not just immediately after the baby's passing, but for several months afterwards.

The loss of a baby can impact on a woman's next pregnancy, making it an understandably anxious time. A British study found that women who'd experienced stillbirth were at higher risk of depression and anxiety in their subsequent pregnancy. Those who'd become pregnant again within 12 months of losing their baby appeared especially vulnerable — remaining more anxious and depressed even after the birth of a healthy child. Whilst grieving parents may be keen to replace their lost child as soon as possible, this study suggests it might, if possible, be better to allow some time to mourn before trying to conceive again.[6]

One very brave mother has shared her story with us and explains how the impact of loss may not hit when we expect it.

When my daughter was stillborn at 21 weeks in 2005 it was a time of both crushing grief and an almost otherworldly sense of love. I put this down to the fact that I received excellent care from the professionals who looked after me — doctors, midwives, social workers, funeral home staff — as well as my family and friends. I felt that I was able to adequately cope with this most tragic of circumstances. And so for a long time I went about my business — working, caring for my two young children, doing all the things I'd done before — to all intents and purposes being a brave, strong, capable woman.

I read all the grief and counselling literature I was given but was never professionally diagnosed with a mental health issue. I guess I felt that I was immune to depression; I had a real sense of gratitude for the blessings I had already been given.

It's really only been this year — five years down the track — that I have reached out for professional help for my mental health. While there is an array of issues in my life, a lot of them stem back to the loss of my third child, which has been compounded by the half a dozen miscarriages I have had since my daughter's birth. It's now highly unlikely that I will have a third child, and this has meant I am at a point of re-assessing my identity. Who am I now? I thought I'd still be mothering small children, being busy with their needs, being enveloped in baby days and toddler times. Now that I'm not doing this an unexpected void has opened up. Discovering how to fill it is my challenge. It turns out that almost everything you read about grief is true — it turns your world upside down in ways you can't even anticipate, it hits you in the back of your psyche when you least expect it and it changes the game plan you thought you had carefully constructed. The result is an almost inevitable burden on your mental health.

*I still haven't been diagnosed with depression but my current
counsellor is keeping an eye on my situation. I have no desire
to be medicated but I'm proud that I have reached out and am
being proactive in my approach to mental health. To me it is as
essential as eating well, exercising and the myriad other things
we must do to stay well.*

There are many support organisations devoted to the support of
families who have lost a baby through stillbirth, neonatal death or
miscarriage. These people know the devastating impact of infant
loss and can help you through the most difficult of times.

- The Stillbirth Foundation **www.stillbirthfoundation.org.au**
- The Stillbirth Alliance **www.stillbirthalliance.org.au**
- SANDS Australia **www.sands.org.au** or **13 000 72637**
- Bonnie Babes Foundation **www.bbf.org.au**

11
HAVING ANOTHER BABY

I was reluctant for a long time to have another child as I was so terrified of getting postnatal depression again. Happily, I have a four-week old baby boy and so far no signs of depression and I'm having a really positive experience this time round. There is a four year gap though between our children as it took me that long for my husband to convince me to go again!

The decision to have another baby is always a big one, regardless of whether or not you've experienced a perinatal mood disorder. Bringing a new life into the world is a wonderful privilege but it comes with costs attached — financial, emotional and physical — as any lifelong commitment does. And if, for you, pregnancy and motherhood have been more about tears and anxiety than the contented bliss you expected, the thought of having another baby may be particularly worrying.

Some women may be so scarred by their previous experiences that they will decide not to have any more children, and that's an understandable choice. However, many other women and their partners will want to add to their family and this chapter is designed to address some of their concerns.

WHAT ARE THE RISKS OF RECURRENCE?

I haven't had another baby yet, and it's quite likely that it won't happen. I have a wonderful relationship with my beautiful, amazing little girl, and I can't help but think of how she would be impacted if I became that unwell again.

If you've previously experienced perinatal anxiety and depression are you at increased risk of recurrence with subsequent babies?

The short answer is yes. One study found that women who experienced depression after a pregnancy had a much higher risk (41% versus 12%) of developing postnatal depression after a subsequent pregnancy than a group of controls (women with no history of depression).[1]

This was a small study so it's probably not worth getting too hung up on the actual numbers, just be mindful that you have a greater risk of developing anxiety and depression with your next baby than you would have if you'd never had a perinatal mood disorder before.

That's the bad news.

The good news we can glean from this study is that you *may not* necessarily go on to develop perinatal anxiety and depression with your next pregnancy. What's more, if you plan your next baby carefully you can do a great deal to reduce that risk further.

PLANNING AND PREPARATION IS THE KEY

Think back to what was happening when you first developed perinatal anxiety and depression. For example:

- Did you have enough money to live comfortably?
- Was your relationship with your partner healthy?
- Did you have a well developed network of family or friends, whom you could call on for practical and emotional support?
- Did you have a good GP?
- Did you have a trusted counsellor you could talk to?
- Did you have a clear understanding of the demands of motherhood?
- Did you know how to ask for help?

For most of you the answer to at least one of these questions will probably be no. If you are planning to have another baby what you need to do is make sure the same problems aren't all present the second time around.

Easier said than done, you might say.

Of course, life is messy and we can't plan for everything, especially when it comes to home finances, but if you can approach your next pregnancy with a support network in place, a doctor who understands your history, and some forewarning of the signs of depression and anxiety, you will still be in a better place than you were the last time around.

HOW LONG TO WAIT?

To reduce the chance of recurrence it's recommended that you wait until you are recovered before trying for another baby. 'Recovered' is, of course, a subjective term, but women who have emerged out the other side of perinatal anxiety and depression often describe it as feeling like their 'old self' again. The people around you, partners, family members, and professionals such as counsellors, will also generally be able to sense the change in you.

How long this will take is variable; in the study quoted earlier, three to six months postnatally was the average time to recovery, but a substantial number of women may still remained depressed after one year.

PANDA suggests waiting six to twelve months after you've been successfully weaned off antidepressants before trying to conceive.[2]

HOW YOUR DOCTOR CAN HELP

If you haven't already done so, we recommend you talk to your doctor about contraception, so that if you do have another baby it comes when you're completely well, and your life circumstances are more favourable.

If you accidentally fall pregnant before you've fully recovered from a bout of anxiety and depression you will need to work closely with your doctor and counsellor to manage your condition, as this may become more challenging. As we discussed earlier, untreated or inadequately treated anxiety and depression during pregnancy may have negative effects on the developing foetus.

IF YOU'RE TAKING ANTIDEPRESSANTS

Contraception is especially important if you are taking an antidepressant. Whilst most of the current information we have about antidepressants and birth defects is reassuring (see Chapter 7), the decision on whether or not to remain on an antidepressant throughout your next pregnancy should be a carefully thought out one, not one that is forced upon you by circumstances.

Unfortunately, when confronted with an unplanned pregnancy, it's very common for women to stop taking their antidepressants abruptly. This rarely pans out well. An American study of 200 pregnant women with a history of depression found that women who discontinued their antidepressant were *five times* more likely to relapse than women who maintained their antidepressant throughout their pregnancy. Moreover, of those who discontinued their medication, six out of ten found it necessary to reintroduce their antidepressant at some stage during the pregnancy.[3]

For women with bipolar disorder who stop their medications when they find out they're pregnant the relapse rate is high and the consequences, such as mania, particularly serious.[4] As discussed in Chapter 7, the management of bipolar disorder in pregnancy is a special case, requiring treatment from a psychiatrist, and for the most part is beyond the scope of this book.

Therefore, if you are currently taking an antidepressant and are planning another baby, it is very important that you have a detailed discussion with your GP or psychiatrist about the risks and benefits of continuing treatment. Please don't rely on the internet or well-meaning friends as your sources of information.

If, after weighing up the pros and cons, you elect to discontinue your antidepressant before trying to conceive, you should be weaned off the medication slowly under a doctor's supervision. Your doctor should also arrange to see you regularly before, during and after pregnancy to closely monitor your mood, and possibly arrange some talking therapy for you as a safeguard.

You may wish to talk to your doctor about recommencing medication soon after the delivery of your next baby. In this situation your doctor may suggest you use one of the antidepressants preferred in breastfeeding. Alternatively, you may elect to bottle feed (either choice is ok). However, the main problem with this approach is that antidepressants can take several weeks to reach their maximal effect and you could be left without cover during a vulnerable period.

My GP suggested I stay on the antidepressants I'm on because of how I'm feeling. She actually advised me to stay on them until we are well and truly finished having kids (because of my history of depression which makes me high risk for postnatal depression). I was hoping to be off these antidepressants before having another baby, but I'm not sure that that will happen.

For women experiencing ongoing problems with anxiety

HAVING ANOTHER BABY **199**

and depression it may not be possible for them to cease their antidepressants, yet they may still desire to have another baby. We discuss the use of antidepressants in pregnancy in Chapter 7. For those who elect to continue their medication, regular check-ups with your obstetrician or midwife and a detailed 19-week ultrasound can help provide some peace of mind.

IF YOU'RE NOT TAKING ANTIDEPRESSANTS

Even if you've recovered sufficiently so that you no longer need antidepressants — or, alternatively, never took them in the first place — this doesn't mean you won't require close monitoring during and after your next pregnancy.

It is recommended you check in with your GP regularly before and after the birth. Your obstetrician or midwife should also be made aware of your history so that they can keep a close eye on your mental and physical wellbeing, help plan a birth that is as controlled and supportive as possible, and ideally organise a longer stay in hospital after delivery, to make sure you're ok. Having regular contact with a child health nurse during the early weeks after delivery may also prove beneficial.

FOREWARNED IS FOREARMED

That's the medical side. How else can you reduce your chance of developing perinatal anxiety and depression again, or at least reduce its impact?

In many ways all the answers are in the preceding chapters:
- having realistic expectations of motherhood
- getting some pre-emptive psychological help and counselling if necessary

- enlisting practical and emotional support in the early months
- self-care — getting enough sleep and doing the things you like
- making sure the people around you understand what perinatal anxiety and depression is, and what it looks like.

If your relationship with your partner suffered the last time around, investing in some couple counselling may also be wise.

In summary you need to have a plan.

Shoshana Bennett, author, counsellor and postnatal depression survivor, recommends sitting down with your partner (or if you don't have one, a close family member) and actually *writing* a plan, which includes:

- an honest discussion of your hopes, worries and fears (and those of your partner)
- a list of warning behaviours, specific to you
- a list of respected professionals to call upon
- a list of support people and what they will be doing
- even a sleep and duty roster.[5]

Co-author Seana Smith tells how having an honest discussion with her husband and a plan in place, helped her avert postnatal depression even though she found herself pregnant with twins.

It took me a long time to persuade my husband that another child would be welcome. For years he was dead set against it; in fact, he still has the referral for a vasectomy from his GP.

Anyway, I found myself pregnant with twins and this gave us both a huge shock. I was over 40 and one of our two older boys already had additional needs. We wanted to do everything we possibly could to keep these twins safely in the womb and I think that set up some good habits of self-care for me.

My husband had been pretty hopeless when I had depression after the birth of my second son. I was diagnosed and treated for postnatal depression but probably had had untreated depression after the birth of our first son and had been in distress when pregnant with our second. I had felt terribly alone — of course I did — a new immigrant with all my family and old friends literally on the other side of the world.

We knew how debilitating my depression had been and how devastating the effect on our relationship. We only managed to stay together through exhaustion, I'm sure. After couple counselling, we had a much clearer idea of what our individual issues had been.

A few years had passed and we were getting on well again. We're a good team when we put our minds to it and we came up with lots of ideas about how to keep me mentally well, which also involved keeping his mental health good too, of course. Mainly this meant getting extra help with the older boys and with the housework.

'Let's do anything we need to do to get through this' was our attitude. 'This is no time to think about trying to reduce the mortgage.'

I sometimes wonder whether it wasn't a blessing to have been pregnant with twins, I don't know that I would have taken so much care of myself if it had been one baby. But I do think that was the key, taking good care of myself and having a person who was there to 'mother the mother'... and that's not a job a father can do; being a father and a husband is enough, at least for my husband.

Anyway, I did get great support and I learned that the emotional support was just as important for me as the practical help. I found a really lovely lady to come to work with our family, an older lady who has the most wonderful, warm and loving nature. She rolled up her sleeves and got on with all the things that need to be done in a busy household, but she also truly loved my family.

When the twins were born, she adored them and I always knew they were in wonderful hands when with her. It was so much more than nannying, it is the nearest we have come to having a granny. That is what really made the difference for me: that practical help wrapped up with love. We still see her a lot.

Managing to NOT become overwhelmed and depressed was a big achievement, I think. I'm so glad it worked out as the disruption of having twins was huge, especially for the big boys. They needed what little time they got with their mum to be happy time.

But as an aside, although I can look back — still surprised really — and say that the first year of the twins' life was a happy year, I have been treated for depression since then.

When the twins were two, we were doing renovations and foolishly stayed in the house, then my husband started working away from home for long stretches, and my mood began to slide. Luckily I could feel this happening and did get to the GP early, before it got too bad.

One January, I just talked to her about how I was feeling and had a couple of appointments with a psychologist. By the end of February I knew where I was heading and started taking an antidepressant. I hadn't liked taking medication at all the first time around, but seven years later and with four kids, no family in Australia and an absent husband... I thought it was just a sensible thing to do. I had to be pragmatic.

There has been no shame or guilt this time: I must be older and wiser. In a quiet way, I feel terribly proud of myself for having avoided sliding too far down that slope into the black pit of depression. I had been there before and had found it a scary place to be.

Sooner or later, I will wean myself off the medication. In the meantime, I can describe myself as 'pharmaceutically enhanced'. I'll hopefully wean myself onto more exercise, more relaxation and more peace and quiet. But there's no rush this time. And I hope I can keep a relationship with my psychologist, difficulties will pop up in life at random intervals and it's so beneficial to talk over tough times with an expert.

PANDA have also produced a fact sheet: *Having another baby after depression*, which tells more women's stories of having another baby after perinatal anxiety and depression. Visit www.panda.org. au.

WHAT IF ALL THIS PLANNING DOESN'T WORK? WHAT IF I STILL DEVELOP PERINATAL ANXIETY AND DEPRESSION AGAIN?

Yes, that is a possibility. You may plan everything to the nth degree, but when baby comes still find yourself subject to the same low moods and anxiety you thought had gone away. As we discussed in Chapter 3, it appears there is a small group of women for whom perinatal anxiety and depression may be genetic and possibly hormonal in origin.

However, even if this does happen, you will still be in a better place than you were last time around. If you've planned ahead, you, and the people around you, will be able to recognise the warning signs quickly and know that you need to get help, and soon. The sooner you get treatment, the faster your recovery will be the second time around. And that's good news.

12
HOW TO HELP — ADVICE FOR FAMILY AND FRIENDS

When my mother came to visit she was fantastic and I cried every time she left (she had to return home as she was still working!)

There is no way that we would have coped without the help of the grandparents. They helped us with everything. Cooking food, looking after the children and sometimes even laundry.

Very often, for the family and friends of those experiencing anxiety and depression, it is terribly hard to know *how* to help. You might not know whether your loved one actually needs help, they may appear to not want any help at all… how are you supposed to know what to do, far less how to do it?

We wanted to find a lot of really good ideas for family and friends, so that they might be able to assist as much as they would like and are able to. First of all we asked professionals, people like psychologists, doctors and midwives, who often find themselves supporting families and friends. Then we interviewed many people who have come out of depression and anxiety who could give their ideas and experiences. As you will see, some things get the thumbs up, and some the thumbs down.

THE PROFESSIONALS' ADVICE

Always start with listening not talking, then follow up with genuine empathy if you can. Something honest that sounds like a friend and not like something out of a counselling book like 'boy, sounds like you've had a s**t of a time' or something that acknowledges that things are NOT a total mess, 'I can't believe that you've held it together through all this'.

Recognise that they need practical day-to-day help delivered without judgement as well as emotional support. A lot of women struggle with asking for help because they might believe it is a sign of failure. That support might be giving them time to sleep, getting fresh food into the house, washing and cleaning.

Other women who might be highly anxious often have trouble sleeping so making them sleep will be a source of irritation. She might benefit from some exercise, massage or other ways to have an hour to herself. If they are really stuck and can't get moving, getting them moving will need to be a focus of therapy.

Over this time, helpers might need to be a bit tough skinned and have the ability to understand that any resistance or anger directed at them is likely to be the illness talking. It will feel easier to walk away, but the woman will likely be very appreciative in the long run that you stuck around through the hard stuff. Usually isolation worsens the condition and unfortunately happens a lot.

At the same time, you can explain how you would like to be treated in this interchange. Realise that it doesn't have to be just you supporting the person. Direct them for care and also get support yourself if you need it. It is depressing looking after a depressed person. Often carers can develop the same symptoms and need their own help.

❧

As the very best model for families, I recommend Amador and Rosen's **When Someone You Love is Depressed.** *I think the most important thing is that, as partners care, they don't overlook their own needs.*

❧

You can help by:
- *allowing the woman space to talk about her feelings without criticising, discounting or dismissing them*
- *offering practical support without taking over and undermining her confidence*
- *encouraging them to talk to GPs, ECHC nurses and to seek counselling.*

❧

My advice is:
- *read*
- *understand*
- *offer to take the baby*
- *spend time*
- *laugh.*

❧

Support women without being judgemental. Tell them if you

are worried about them and why. Give them a lot of positive encouragement around what they are doing well.

GENERAL ADVICE FROM PARENTS

Here are some thoughts from people who have experienced perinatal anxiety and depression.

I encourage family and friends to ring PANDA (see page 275), mainly because I didn't and I wish now that I had. I encourage people even if they are struggling with a number of seemingly unrelated issues that affects their mood and motivation to call or to speak to their doctor or child health nurse because it's best to be sure. There just may be some little bit of information, help or advice that they could get by speaking to someone about their struggle, even if they are not depressed, and that could just be the thing they needed. Or even if they think they might have it, to just speak up and get it checked out. No loss if they don't have perinatal depression, but a chance to catch it, if they have.

Encourage them to ask for help when they need it. Empathise, share with them that it's a really tough job that we were never meant to do alone, so if they have people they can ask for help, they definitely should ask and not to feel bad about it. Offer to be a sympathetic ear, or to visit and help out where you can. Offer to find help for them.

- *Someone who has depression does not want to hear about your experience.*
- *They don't want to be told that they are experiencing normal every day adjustment.*

- *They want you to listen, to be a shoulder to cry on, and not provide anything other than love.*
- *Don't judge as the new mum will already be so hard on herself.*
- *Accept that the depression is there and help them navigate the health services and support as the mum may not be able to do this herself.*
- *Ask the mum what sort of help she wants, and if she cannot tell you, just go ahead and give help where it is needed.*
- *Don't try and 'fix' the depression as without the doctors etc you will in all likelihood fail.*
- *Find out what makes them the most anxious and provide support in those areas. It might be the bathing, the nappy changing, the settling when baby is crying.*
- *Be flexible and watch for areas where you might be able to lend a hand.*
- *Don't wait to be invited.*
- *Ask the health workers how they think you can help.*

- *Take them to a good GP for referral to appropriate services and/or medication.*
- *Suggest a postnatal depression support group in their area or a postnatal depression phone support line.*
- *It may take a few goes to get the right medication. They WILL get better with treatment.*
- *Give practical support, eg babysitting, cooking etc.*
- *Don't judge them or analyse why they have postnatal depression.*
- *Reassure them it's temporary and they won't always feel like this.*
- *Take a day at a time.*
- *Stay with them if they are scared to be alone with baby.*
- *Don't make them feel guilty or suggest they don't love their child.*

- *Take them on outings out of the house to somewhere uplifting.*
- *Give literature on perinatal depression symptoms etc so they can see if it relates to their feelings.*
- *Help them to get professional help.*
- *Be available to make doctors' appointments, go with them to appointments.*
- *Spend as much time with them as possible without taking over.*
- *The mum needs to feel in control as much as possible, go along for the ride (eg help put out the washing while she feeds the baby or offer to mind baby while she has a sleep).*
- *Try to be understanding about the changes that have taken place in mum's life and be sympathetic.*
- *Don't judge when they do open up and tell you how they really feel.*
- *Don't freak out. Help out!*

Educate yourself and provide practical support but don't take over. Empower the mum but do not overpower her.
Read booklets, call support lines, find specialised counsellors or psychologists. Join an organisation such as PANDA or From The Heart WA and ARAFMI (see Resources Guide).

My husband is great! He also has been finding it a big change suddenly being a parent, so it's great that we're on the same journey together. He has supported me whenever I've gone to see the GP or psychologist. He's told me I'm doing the right thing getting help. He tells me everyday that I'm a good mummy which is encouraging.

Three things stood out more than anything else... babysitting, cooking us meals and telling us we are good parents and were doing a good job.

✤

Be there for them. Help them in gentle, caring, practical ways (cook them a meal, grab them some milk and bread from the shop, bring them a bunch of flowers, babysit for them).

✤

Ask them how you can help.

✤

Congratulate them on their successes and for being a good parent. Don't judge them or compare them to other parents. Don't tell them 'you shouldn't be feeling like this'. Gently remind them how normal they are and tell them how wonderful they are. Tell them they are a good mum/dad.

✤

Take it seriously if they mention thoughts of suicide.

✤

Find ways to help them, eg look up websites/helplines for support for them that they may not know about.

✤

Be there for them, ie to listen and not be judgemental.

✤

- *BUCKETS OF LOVE, LOADS OF PATIENCE AND TONS OF SUPPORT.*
- *Practical help, housework, cooking, driving kids to school, taking kids overnight etc.*
- *Being proactive and reading up on perinatal depression.*
- *Don't turn a blind eye, sit in denial or get out the old school 'pull your socks up' number. This is damaging and hurtful.*
- *A BIG HUG GOES A LONG WAY...*

THE MOST HELPFUL THINGS

These were the helpful things that people did for us:
- *Dropping off meals or coming over to cook a meal and eat with us.*
- *One friend sent me text messages every day with funny comments about how crap it was having a newborn which made me feel less alone.*
- *Others sent text messages and emails letting me know they were there.*
- *Dropping off cakes/muffins.*
- *Giving me bath products to help me relax.*
- *Just knowing that friends were there if I needed them.*

The single most important person to my recovery was my Mum though. She looked after me, making sure I ate my meals, got outside, had a shower etc. She took over some of the baby chores that I felt incapable of doing and she made me feel secure while I recovered.

- ***What is helpful is to ask questions. If what you get in response is not 'normal' then help the person get help. The best thing for me was when others organised the doctor's appointment and got me there, looked after the kids, made***

meals, came over to visit for a chat, helped tidy up mess (even if I said don't bother).
- *Talk about it and be sympathetic, but don't give advice if you have no experience with depression. You may think you are helping but you are probably doing the opposite.*

What was helpful was my cousin coming in to the house. Despite how miserable and negative and tired I was, she just went about cleaning and preparing me some food, and bringing me cups of tea and glasses of water and insisting I sit down and rest while the girls were asleep. Just getting on with doing what needed to be done, playing with the girls and modelling ways of interacting with them positively, even when they were being 'difficult'. Getting a bottle of expressed breast milk from the fridge, warming it up, taking a baby from me and feeding her rather than letting me struggle with getting her to feed from the breast.

AND THE LEAST HELPFUL THINGS

The unhelpful things were:
- *My husband organised a brunch to show off our new baby when she was about three weeks old. This was the worst possible thing he could have done as I had to use all my energy to try and put on a brave face and it had a huge negative impact on my confidence.*
- *I found seeing other 'happy' new mums really unhelpful.*

Comments like 'you're doing a great job', 'you'll be fine, you're just tired' etc when someone tells you they aren't coping are not at all helpful.

By the time someone says this, the chances are they are really not coping. This may not manifest as a dirty house or an unwashed mum or baby. This is often an internal thing. Feelings of despair, hopelessness, not wanting to 'do this' any more...

What was not helpful for me was for people to point the finger and attempt to name what I was experiencing as postnatal depression. **What was helpful (or would have been) was for people to listen to me, endlessly if necessary, about how hard I was finding things. I found this a method of support and care and it helped.**

What was not helpful was my mother constantly analysing 'why' I had postnatal depression eg hormones/having surgery after the birth/having a girl, etc etc!! She fell in a bit of a heap herself instead of being strong and suggesting what to do to get better. Considering she had had postnatal depression herself I thought she would have been a bit more clued up! However, she was good with practical things eg cooking, which was a big help.

Also unhelpful are well-meaning comments from friends, eg someone said to me the other day 'you know now that it wasn't your fault you got it (postnatal depression) first time around, don't you... I knew you'd be a good mother this time'. Well, I never thought it was my fault and I was a good mother first time around too, thanks very much!!

What didn't help was people insisting on coming around to see

the girls and bring them presents at times that weren't convenient for us. People saying they would come and help or visit or ring and then not doing any of those things. Having to ask for help, or for people to come over and no-one coming. Two people came once, experienced the screaming, and never came back or called me again. I was left feeling guilty for not ringing them to thank them again for coming around. One friend came and brought a book, but then expected to be fed... and it turned out she was there to see my cousin.

My mother's self-absorbed behaviour also didn't help, she added to my burden. This was particularly disappointing because I remember her suffering postnatal depression with my youngest brother (I was seven years old). All she said was 'I had postnatal depression with Daniel' — end of discussion. My parents didn't help by making comments like 'just do 'this' or 'that' ie just ring the council and ask them to send some help... Just give her a bottle, there's nothing wrong with it... you should be happy, you have two beautiful, healthy babies. When I told my uncle that I was going to see the doctor because I was depressed, his response was 'do you want me to slap you?'

ADVICE FOR PARTNERS

I have two friends in the same boat, we're all far away from our families, and the three of us are all strong women. So we said to each other: Are we not getting enough support from our husbands?'

Our husbands' ideas of supporting us is to say 'oh you're feeling like this, let me go and do the washing up for you or let me fix whatever's wrong'.

But it's not what we needed… we just wanted them to say 'darling come here, let me give you a cuddle', or 'let me make you a cup of tea, you sit down', or 'don't worry, I'll take the children to playgroup tomorrow' or whatever it might be.

We wanted to have some emotional support rather than the physical let-me-fix-this-issue approach, because a lot of the time it's not the actual issue that we are ranting and raving about which is making us break down, it's more just everything on top of us and one thing's just the final straw.

AND A BLOKE ON HELPING OTHER BLOKES…

If you sense that someone is overwhelmed or seems down or withdrawn, tell them about PANDA (see page 275) or encourage them to talk to their GP. Aussie blokes care about their mates, so if you've got a mate who needs to talk or needs help or support, for goodness sake don't stand back and let their lives deteriorate.

Try not to be judgemental — it really adds to the pressure. Let mum be mum to her baby. Believe it or not, she knows best.

The personal stories of mothers and fathers dealing with perinatal anxiety and depression can be so open to judgement. How often are women told:
- 'pull yourself together, we all have issues'.
- 'stop being so self absorbed and get over yourself, you have

so many things to be thankful for'.

- 'mothers these days are so precious, they expect so much, it was so much harder in my day yet we never complained'.
- 'you mothers are just a bunch of whingeing women who have no idea how lucky you are'.
- 'what are you complaining about? You get to lie around the house all day and play with the baby while I go to work'.

If a mother is anxious or depressed, these statements are completely unhelpful and irrelevant. If a mother or father is unwell, this sort of advice, no matter how well-meaning, will not help. Unfortunately financial security, strong relationships and fulfilling careers are not protection against perinatal anxiety and depression. Privileged or disadvantaged, teenager or 43 year old, fifth-generation white Australian or newly-arrived migrant, all types of women can be affected by the damage caused through mental health problems during this time.

The complexities of anxiety and depression can also add to the difficulties of understanding the issues that individuals might be dealing with. Scepticism and misinformation occur throughout our society.

A bit of humanity can go a long way: random acts of kindness — a meal, babysitting, a coffee, a walk, a talk, etc. We've all had horrible feelings at some time during our mothering experiences. We all know the value of a friend who will listen.

13
LOOKING BACK ON IT NOW — PERSONAL STORIES AND REFLECTIONS

There is a history of mental health issues in my family but I had no history of anxiety or depression before or during my pregnancy. I was mostly happy and not stressed and the pregnancy was normal. I first became mentally unwell at age 38, one week after my daughter's birth.

I received no information on mood disorders. No health professional asked me if I had any psychiatric history or if my family had any psychiatric history. I would have told them that all of my siblings had had depression and psychosis, and that a brother and sister had bipolar.

The midwife who took our antenatal classes did mention perinatal depression and I asked her if I was high risk as I was a little worried. She said as I had always been ok not to worry, I would be ok. She mentioned postnatal psychosis but said: 'Don't worry, none of you will get that as it is very rare'.

I had spent very little time in my whole life ever thinking about life with a baby. I did not really think I would ever get the opportunity to be a mother. However, I embraced the pregnancy and looked forward to having my little girl. I regret not spending some time thinking about motherhood and my life.

I also regret not spending time considering fatherhood and my husband and how he would be. I regret not having a support network organised to help me at the time of birth. Unfortunately I was a very independent person who was not welcome to the idea of needing help. I assumed I would relish the challenge of motherhood as I had enjoyed life challenges previously.

The birth of my daughter was fairly traumatic. I was given pethidine and gas which seemed to do nothing to ease the pain. My daughter went to ICU straight after her birth as she had foetal distress.

I did not feel ready to go home three days after the birth of my baby. Physically, I could barely walk, I had not been able to bath my baby and mentally I felt overwhelmed before I left the hospital. I told the nurses I was not ready to go home but they said there was no medical reason to keep me.

One week after my daughter's birth I was diagnosed with postnatal psychosis. This turned into postnatal depression with psychotic thoughts. I was admitted to a psychiatric unit at the same hospital where I had given birth one week earlier. I started on antidepressants about a month later, after the depression deepened to a point where I hardly spoke or moved at all. I went into a deeper and deeper depression.

It felt like I was in a black sea drowning and I wanted to get to the surface but I couldn't see which way was up, so I didn't even know which way to start swimming. The black sea at night with no guiding light is the only way I would describe my depression. I felt so anxious all the time that adding even one more decision would tip me over the edge so easily.

I had delusions concerning the health of my baby or my own health. I would wake up with very confusing thoughts. I felt very agitated but depressed. I couldn't sleep much at all. I couldn't think very well and I had trouble coping with motherhood. I felt powerless, useless, hopeless and most of all completely overwhelmed by my life.

I was not safe around my baby. This was the reason for my first admission. At the time of my second admission, I thought my whole family was in danger from me. The third time I was extremely suicidal — a goodbye letter was written to my family and friends. I also had a method planned with date/time etc all organised. I presume I was considered extremely high risk so I was admitted, without my baby at this stage, to a depression unit. After a couple of weeks my baby joined me in the mother and baby unit at the psychiatric unit.

I felt safe from the outside world, I still was not myself but it felt like an oasis compared to being at home. I wished friends would come to visit but nobody did. I wished family would visit but they didn't. Still, I would recommend it as a place to get better.

The antipsychotics worked like tranquilisers and helped me to feel calmer and to sleep. I felt almost normal on these but I was taken off them very quickly and then put on antidepressants which I don't feel helped. I was on different antidepressants for a few months. I was re-admitted to another psych hospital where I found one psychiatrist who listened when I talked about symptoms/feelings. This doctor and ECT for my severe depression made recovery finally occur.

*I met many psychiatrists, nurses and psychologists while in
hospital and as an outpatient. They were mostly polite and tried to
be supportive. However, they did not listen to how I was feeling,
they liked to tell me how I was feeling. This was not helpful for
the long-term recovery.*

This is a list of treatments I had:
- *Antidepressant — somewhat helpful, some types*
- *Hospital admission — very helpful*
- *Counselling — helpful*
- *ECT — very helpful*
- *Antipsychotics (tranquilisers) — very helpful.*

*As I always seemed more anxious than typically depressed I feel
the tranquilisers really did work well and combined with the
antidepressants did a much better job than just the antidepressants
alone.*

*I really feel the best treatment was finding a health professional
who was prepared to listen to me. Prior to this nobody listened,
they just told me how I was feeling, as if I was a line in a
textbook.*

*The next best thing was meeting other mothers with depression
who were also not coping. I no longer felt so alone and so freaky.
If they could keep going so could I. Meeting another woman who
had previously been very depressed and had recovered helped a
lot.*

*Looking back now, I can absolutely see that my family of origin
issues were involved. My childhood was very sad and quite
dysfunctional. My parents never showed any love or support and
we children did not feel wanted, loved or cared for, although we
did have food and a roof. My siblings had all experienced mental
health problems and I was the last one to suffer. I felt I could not
be a mother as I did not know what to do. I had no role model to*

follow. I still do the opposite to what my mother would do.

Looking back, I could have dealt better with my situation by not trying to listen to everybody and follow everybody's advice. I would have been better to follow my heart. Despite knowing I was mentally unwell and could not think clearly, this did not mean I could not think at all. It was just harder, like thinking with a hangover. My thinking ability was severely impaired but not non-existent. Nobody gave me credit to think at all.

Family support would have helped. It was not offered and I did not feel I needed it. Even when I was not coping I still didn't want help. I wanted my husband to help and offer support but unfortunately he was unable to be supportive. He had no idea he was not helping, he thought he was supportive. I needed reassurance that I would get through it and that I would recover and go on to be a great mum.

I also needed more practical things done like washing, cooking, cleaning, painting, backyard clearing, so I could spend more time with my baby and learn to enjoy being with her. Instead I had to do 99% of all housework and so had no time to build rapport with her. I needed someone to reassure me I would recover and be ok, reassure me I was actually doing a good job as a mum.

If I had had a helpful, supportive husband that would have helped me. Support is crucial to mental wellbeing. The support required is different for each person and can be practical, physical, emotional or just knowing somebody is there who understands how difficult it is for you at the moment.

After this experience of postnatal psychosis and depression, I am a better person. I mean more compassionate and understanding. I am a stronger person, I know I can cope with lots of adversity and still come through it. I am more confident. I have no pretences to the world — I am just me, exactly how I am, and proud.

My daughter and I survived. Every day is fantastic to me as I survived a life threatening experience. I relish each and every day as a bonus in my life and I enjoy my daughter's company and watching her grow.

Finding others who have shared the same or similar difficulties is essential to ongoing mental wellbeing. I see meeting others with similar experiences as part of the recovery process. There are many more women out there but they do not talk about it as they feel a sense of shame. Speak up to de-stigmatise.

These are my thoughts on what to do if you may be at risk:
- *find out risk percentage as early as possible*
- *take as many precautions as possible if the risk is high*
- *be ever vigilant if a few down days turn into something worse*
- *have some wellbeing strategies ready to put in place asap if your mental health is deteriorating*
- *talking about negative thoughts or even having negative thoughts does not mean you have to act on them*
- *never act on the negative thoughts*
- *for every negative thought take a positive action.*

Many people never think they are at risk and they don't want help, but help needs to be given anyway. Most women are not aware they could have a problem as they see it as a sign of weakness.

I think that at all mothers' group early childhood centres they should place as much emphasis on preventing depression as they do on promoting breastfeeding. Early childhood nurses and GPs need much more training in recognising symptoms of anxiety and depression. Referrals are essential.

What I'd like to see put in place:
- *screening all mothers for risk of perinatal depression*
- *careful monitoring of high risk mothers*

- GPs stressing that it is quite common to experience depression and that there is no shame in needing help
- ads on TV with a slogan eg 'If you have a negative thought, take a positive action. Never act on negative thoughts'.

Looking back on what happened, I can honestly say that in a strange sort of way I am glad to have been through that depression.

I think I have a lot more insight now into the depths of peoples' emotions and much more empathy as well. It started me on a search for finding my true self which helps me to look at the world and things going on around me in a very different way to the last 35 years.

I am no longer held ransom by my thoughts, but can choose what to believe and how to act. I am learning more and more every day about who I am, not me the mother or the wife or the daughter, just me.

I could have dealt with my postnatal depression better by getting early treatment and accepting that my marriage was a fundamental part of my depression. But now I am out of a desperately lonely marriage, have two amazing boys and am free to love and enjoy them.

I have learnt so much, about how we can cope and how we grow and change, how we can 'change' the past. My advice? Don't lock yourself away, talk to someone, don't cover it up.

It would have helped:
- *to have friends with babies, I was very alone*

- *to go back to work earlier*
- *having more support.*

The good clearly outweighs the bad in terms of what I have learnt. But the bad points are that if my postnatal depression — and indeed antenatal depression — had been recognised by someone (including myself) sooner and I'd have got help sooner, I may have been able to resolve my breastfeeding issues before they got out of control. Most importantly, I might have been able to enjoy the first precious months of my children's lives rather than having only bad or at best really vague memories and reminders.

The other bad thing is that I might have had the strength and confidence to ask for help and to inform the few people closest to me who were willing to help, what was going on. AND my husband might not have suffered so much in silence.

The good points I guess are everything else that I gained: knowledge, understanding, resilience, strength, motivation and determination.

I am stronger and more confident and capable than I've ever been in my life as a result of postnatal depression and managing it whilst learning to bring up two new people at once! What a herculean task, and I've done it. AND I was able to complete the final year of my social work degree full-time last year without dropping in my grade average from my unfettered pre-children years of study.

I have so much more understanding and empathy for the thankless and isolating task of parenting babies and young children, especially mothering. I have learnt that mothers, as a result of their mothering experience, can be some of the wisest and strongest people in our society, and thus grossly undervalued and misunderstood.

I have learnt that anything is possible and that whatever situation you find yourself in, it's never a foregone conclusion. I no longer believe in fate, I have learnt that life is a continuum of endless possibilities and unexpected twists and turns which represent opportunities for continual growth and development.

My sisters and I have all suffered from postnatal depression and antenatal depression too. I was depressed when I was pregnant with my third child. I spoke to my obstetrician who referred me to a psychologist specialising in perinatal depression.

Four months after the birth of my baby, I realised something was wrong as I got severe PMS symptoms that did not go once my period started. I went back to the psychologist I had seen antenatally. I had great support from family.

Looking back on it now, the things I feel important are:
- *to treat perinatal depression as early as possible and don't be ashamed to admit you are depressed and need help*
- *don't say 'it will never happen to me'*
- *have a general understanding of what can happen and if you are in any doubt seek professional help*
- *be prepared for a huge lack of sleep and social changes — the baby becomes the focus and sleep becomes very important as coping mechanisms fail when you are over tired.*

In our society, we need to have greater awareness of how difficult the first three to four months with a new baby are. But, as a result, I have a better understanding of myself and what is important to me.

❧

Postnatal depression has taught me how to ask for help as soon as I feel I need it. I don't let things get out of control and I spend time meditating which I find relaxing. I still have memories that I find confronting and can't quite believe that I was once so unwell. It seems like a bad dream.

My kids seem ok, though we sought counselling for my eldest son. He seemed to need to express his feelings by drawing pictures of himself at school but wanting to be at home to comfort me. He went through a difficult patch at school but came through the other side with the help of professionals, and me realising I needed to reassure him.

My daughter is pretty hardy and seems to have ridden the waves beautifully. My baby boy (now four years old) acts up now to get my attention and this is hard work. My husband is the one who has been most affected; he finds it difficult to talk about that time without getting upset. He coped well during my illness but is still struggling to accept that I am now well. He worries about me and I feel he is now a bit depressed himself.

I am definitely a much stronger person, so many issues have been sorted out through this experience. My relinquishment as a baby, my adoption, incest, miscarriages, the list goes on and I can remember there came a point as I became stronger that I thought to myself, hey you really don't have much left to deal with. This was a turning point for me and though it was hard work I wouldn't change anything. I feel a lightness and freedom that has been missing all my life; it doesn't get much better than that.

❧

I think it's hard to look back and say I learnt something positive about having postnatal depression because it is not a nice experience, not at all. However, I do think I have learnt not to have assumptions about life. You never know or can't assume that tomorrow will be the same as yesterday, or even that you are as strong as you think you are.

I have more of an understanding of other people and what their challenges may be, not only with postnatal depression but anxiety and a range of other things. I believe I really understand what other mums who have postnatal depression are going through, and have a lot of compassion for them, which helps me with the telephone counselling.

I hope my daughters don't have to go through the same as me because there's a possibility of it being passed down in some way. At least if they do I know so much more about it now.

I think unless you have had postnatal depression or something like that, you can never really, really understand what it is like, or even the depths of desperation someone might feel. It changed me so that I can now understand how it is for others. I have no criticism of people who get driven to the edge so to speak because I understand what that feels like. I understand that it is such a fine line between being sane and feeling like you could hurt your child.

I think I may have had a superior attitude before but not any more. This is positive for me because I want to become a counsellor and I believe it will help me considerably in my career.

My experience taught me to be generous with myself. That is, lower my expectations, accept that I am not a super-person able to do everything, and that I have limits. Probably it was my scare after I weaned off the drugs and was in danger of new bouts of depression that was my biggest reality check.

Overall, the experience has changed me enormously. I have a much greater appreciation for perinatal depression and the debilitating effect it can have, and I have also developed an empathy for my friends who suffer from depression and anxiety in their day-to-day lives. I was completely ignorant in the past and it really took my own personal experience to understand.

The only bad point is the sadness that I feel that with both kids I was never actually able to experience the joy of being a new mum. Yet, that really is the only negative that I feel, and I have come to terms with it now, accepting that perinatal depression is just one of the things that makes me a stronger person.

I'm much more empathetic now to people with mental health issues, both in my work and personal life. I realise that you can't 'snap out of it' or talk yourself out of it. I know now how to nurture myself and what helps keep me 'sane', eg strenuous exercise, time out for myself, part-time work, asking for help from others etc.

Getting involved in From the Heart (see page 311) was a good thing that came out of it — I have met some lovely women with whom I'm still friendly and I enjoyed my time as Phone Support Co-ordinator, helping other women going through perinatal depression — it was very rewarding.

It was the worst time of my life and I think I was on the verge of a nervous breakdown. My relationship with my husband and friends suffered. Having my first child was the biggest shock and adjustment of my life.

Also, I discovered there are some awful so-called 'experts' in postnatal depression, who don't have a clue what they're talking about! I had a traumatic time at my daughter's birth (I was diagnosed just before her birth with a serious medical condition and needed surgery a few days after her birth) and the hospital I delivered at should have known I was at high-risk for postnatal depression, yet no-one mentioned it or screened for it (this has since changed, luckily).

I now know that parenting is hard work and women in particular need to be supportive of one another and not judgemental. I really try to not judge other mums and to offer support to those who are struggling. Mums and dads need to do whatever it takes to 'stay sane' and not care what other people think.

Although looking after a baby is hard work, it does get easier with time and becomes so rewarding later on as they get older. My four year old comes out with the most priceless comments and I wouldn't be without her for anything, so the postnatal depression was all worth it. I survived and am stronger for it.

I am much more understanding of people with psychological issues. It is not possible to deny that these types of illnesses are just as real as broken legs or backaches. I am more aware of the impact my thoughts have on my life. I have learnt that I'm not meant to take this journey of life alone, it's much easier with people along for the ride! I'm not infallible. I'm not perfect. I'm an emotional being and that shouldn't be denied.

I am more honest with myself and others about how I really feel and what is really going on in my life. I am more compassionate and understanding. I am much more interested in people. I am kinder to myself.

The bad point about the perinatal depression is the sad realisation that my first-born missed out on so much in the first year until I got back into my groove. The good points are I

am able to share my story of recovery and empathise with mums who are struggling emotionally, to share that we can get better.

It also kick started a career change as I now work both in a paid and voluntary capacity in the perinatal mental health field.

I learnt that it takes a village to raise a child, that motherhood is the best job, a very hard job but full of self-development opportunities. I am truly blessed to have three children that I adore.

Many of us have fantasies and dreams of how our lives will evolve, but life carries with it no guarantees and is full of unexpected twists and turns that we all need to negotiate. This is also the case when it comes to parenthood.

Some of us make plans that are realised but for most of us becoming a family is a very imperfect science: unplanned pregnancies compete with the desperation of trying to become pregnant, unsuccessful IVF cycles and miscarriages leave a trail of devastation for some women, while other women live with the emotional scars of terminations.

In hindsight, I had no idea that my life would be so changed after the birth of my first baby. Nothing prepared me for the emotional roller coaster, the physical exhaustion and the shift in relationships and priorities. Throughout my first pregnancy I was focused on the end game — the birth. It never occurred to me that the birth was in fact the beginning.

Dreams are not a bad thing as long as we are mindful that reality might be different. Unfortunately that is where many of us come unstuck. A flexible approach to our own lives certainly helps when managing our dreams and expectations as we're confronted with reality.

Perinatal anxiety and depression nearly cost me my marriage, it even nearly cost me my life. Many people comment on challenges in their lives as worthwhile experiences as they grew stronger and became wiser. Perhaps I did, but my overall response when I think back to that time of my life is one of overwhelming sadness. I am not glad to have lived through that experience.

Many of the things I learnt about myself and others could have been gleaned through general life experiences. I didn't need to take myself, my husband and my children to hell and back. I didn't need to lose my sanity and my self-esteem in order to grow and mature. I feel that I robbed myself of some special time with my children.

It took many years for my husband and me to rebuild what we lost in the process of perinatal anxiety and depression. Yet, I am very aware how lucky we are as anecdotally there are many stories of significant loss associated with perinatal mood disorders. Some of this loss comes in the form of relationship breakdowns attributed to emotional problems during the perinatal period, and even more shocking are the stories of suicide. I consider myself one of the lucky ones and with that comes the survivors' guilt that I will carry for the rest of my life.

I am forever grateful that I am a mother, and that we have created a family. My children have given me so much joy and a different focus to my life. Now that they are all growing up I feel so blessed. They are funny and irreverent, often exasperating, sometimes challenging. I love them passionately and would protect them fiercely. The special drawings, notes and cards I have received from them over the years are my precious tokens of what I mean to them. I could not imagine my life without my children. They have bought a rich craziness and messiness into my life and I wouldn't have it any other way. I am so profoundly grateful that I have been able to be their mother for all these years.

I can look back as a well woman. I learnt some self-awareness — how to look after myself emotionally, how to be in touch with my inner demons, and how to deal with them when they start to emerge (which they do from time to time). I learnt to understand the triggers that might set me off so I try to manage my life in order to avoid them. Life is far from perfect but it is a journey.

Those early years when our children are young are just a part of the journey. The first few years of parenting babies and young children are very intense and can sometimes be strange as we grow and learn and try to understand the often mysterious role of motherhood. What makes the journey interesting is that the scenery is always changing and just when we think we've got it all under control some unforseen need of a back seat driver forces us to change direction once again.

I feel very lucky to have received the support I did from medical professionals and a few select family and friends. It took a long time, however, for this support to arrive because we didn't have any understanding of what was really going on in our lives. Perinatal mood disorders are a part of life, but the intensity and impact can be ameliorated if parents are educated and have some self-awareness of what is acceptable chaos and what is a potential train wreck, and if medical professionals have the time to listen with their radar alert for the subtext.

It was a random conversation with an insightful doctor that enabled me to get the help I needed. What a fortuitous conversation and what a significant turning point. It changed the path of my life. I was able to receive the help I needed and I eventually recovered. Other women are not so lucky. Many women and their families are left to suffer, sometimes for years.

A diagnosis does not bring with it instant relief, far from it. In fact, in some cases a diagnosis might bring with it more distress. While some women are relieved to find they are struggling with an illness with a name, others are not happy with being 'labelled'. Recovery can take a long time and can be hard work. Most women and their families will struggle for months, some even for years.

We saw a psychologist who treated us as a couple. She saw the issue as one that we needed to work through together. The perspective of this particular psychologist was holistic. She provided us with ideas and we had to undertake 'homework' tasks. Her approach was essentially to use Cognitive Behaviour Therapy (see Chapter 6).

I look back on this counselling as another turning point in my life, not just related to the anxiety and depression. I learnt valuable life skills that will always remain with me. These were skills that may well come naturally to others but that I obviously needed to be taught. The acquisition of these skills has not led to a perfect life, but it has helped me to deal with many imperfect situations.

When speaking to medical professionals or to community groups, I am always surprised by the number of people who come to me afterwards, often quite emotional, to share their story. Perinatal mood disorders are such a common life experience among women and yet many mothers still struggle through this time, often in isolation, too distressed or embarrassed to ask for help, or perhaps unable to find the help that they need.

I hope that there will come a time when mothers in our society are cared for more both physically and emotionally during pregnancy and after they give birth. I hope that the media will resist its need to airbrush or sensationalise motherhood and create a more realistic picture which mothers can relate to rather than compare themselves with unfavourably or judgementally. And I hope that mothers will be more compassionate and less judgemental of each other.

14

STARTING WITH MYSELF — SELF-CARE STRATEGIES FOR A FAMILY, FOR A LIFETIME

Be kind to yourself. Pregnancy and childbirth and those early weeks and months of parenting take a huge physical and emotional toll. Remind yourself that in other cultures and during other times mothers were nurtured, even cocooned during this time. They were not expected to bounce back and start running a house, perhaps caring for other children, cooking, cleaning, socialising and returning to sex goddess status... And don't be misled by the media and others telling you it should all come to you naturally and that it is a breeze. Motherhood is hard work, but with a supportive family and friends it can bring unexpected joys and fulfilment.

I do believe that many of us modern women find this time hard because we often move away from our emotional support. Women used to be around their families a lot more. We had that support... even if it was just emotional support, even if it was just going to Mum's house, to your sister's house or to your aunt's house or another woman in your family to say 'I just need a chat' or 'can I just come round for a cup of tea?'.

This is the mantra that all new mothers need to learn:
- *I do need help!*
- *I can ask for help!*
- *I will ask for help!*

Something else I'm slowly learning to do is to have 'me time' regularly. I find that motherhood is the most amazing job in the world but it is also the most emotionally draining job. In order to be the best mum I can for my daughter, I have to have moments here and there to re-charge my batteries. I've finally come to a point of realising this — now I just have to do it and not feel guilty.

WELCOME TO THE WORLD OF 'MOTHERGUILT'

All mothers feel guilty at some time, some mothers feel guilty all the time. It comes with the territory. Guilt about what you ate or drank during your pregnancy, about birth choices, over time spent (or not) with your baby, partner, friends, family or even yourself. You might experience guilt over work choices, cooking ability or home cleanliness... and on it goes as your baby moves through childhood and on to adolescence. Accept it, try to manage it, try to move on from it, and never give into it. Rather than focussing on perceived shortcomings recognise all the positives that you have contributed to your family in your important role as a mother. Motherhood is not about perfection. It is about being a 'good enough' mother most of the time.

WHAT YOU MIGHT BE EXPERIENCING

I have a little routine now for the times when I can feel I am getting worn down by the rigours of motherhood and family life. Usually I start to feel totally overwhelmed, my head races with thoughts about all the things that need to be done, I panic at the thought of forgetting things like library books, school notes, spare nappies.

That's when I need to start slowing down a lot. I start to walk slowly, to hang up the washing slowly, to shop slowly, even to talk slowly. This helps to stop me falling into a major panic where I rush around like a mad thing. It really is true — and I know this for sure now — that if I slow down and do one thing at a time, I get a lot more done than when I am whizzing about like a maniac.

Then I try to calmly look ahead and start cancelling things. I used to have to do that when I was in a state, but now I do it to stop myself getting into a state. And it works. Better to calmly bail out of things than to wait until I'm incapable.

Motherhood brings with it a mixture of good and bad days. We all have days when we feel totally overwhelmed and exhausted as well as other days when we feel on top of the world. You don't need to be suffering from perinatal anxiety and depression to feel that motherhood is maybe not all it's cracked up to be. Even mentally healthy mothers have days when their babies and young children can drive them to distraction. A useful mantra for these times is 'try not to take yourself too seriously'.

However, some women may experience more than just the

usual emotional ups and downs related to pregnancy and early motherhood. They may experience one or more of the following (see Chapter 2 for more information):

- **Adjustment disorder** — many of us have no real idea of what to expect and can find adjusting to parenthood very confusing.
- **Anxiety disorder** — perhaps a general stomach churning feeling for no particular reason, or perhaps in response to a stressful situation. Two very common types of anxiety which can be experienced during this time are obsessive compulsive disorder and posttraumatic stress disorder.
- **Depression** — generally a low mood although it can sometimes manifest as hyperactivity.
- **Psychosis** — this only affects 1 in 1000 women but is an acute illness requiring immediate medical help.

SELF-CARE

This means looking after your physical and emotional health during pregnancy and throughout motherhood.

Physical self-care

- **Sleep** — always a luxury for parents with babies and toddlers, but our bodies need it.
- **Diet** — of course we know that healthy eating is important, but sometimes a carrot just isn't going to do it for us, sometimes it's just easier and nicer to eat a packet of Tim Tams. Try and make chocolate a one off treat; fresh fruit salad can be a great substitute.
- **Exercise** — yes it's important, but sometimes we just feel too exhausted or we may struggle to find the time. A 20 minute walk with the pram to the shops to buy some bread and milk, or perhaps a regular commitment with a friend is worth the effort.

I eat healthily and exercise (run) as many mornings as I can, as much for my health and fitness as to provide a good example for my children about being healthy and happy. I started a book club to interact with other people (not just mothers!) with similar and not so similar tastes in reading as myself. I also try to have at least one weekend a year away from husband and children to rejuvenate and feel better.

Emotional self-care

- **Sleep** — we all feel better after a good night's sleep: the dramas we ruminate over at 3am tend to disappear after sunrise.
- **Time for yourself** — this is not selfish time. Even grabbing a few minutes by yourself in the bathroom (with your children on the other side of the door) can give you some headspace.
- **Goals** — make them simple and realistic.
- **Exercise** — can help your mind feel better too. Getting out of the house can help clear the cobwebs from your mind, and the endorphins produced by exercise are a great natural mood lifter.
- **Relationships** — these need time. Meet a friend for a coffee, get together with a group of friends (with babies and children for a play, or without for a meal or a book club), find some time to spend with your partner, even if it's on the couch watching a movie on TV.
- **Who am I?** — mother is not the only definition. While being a mother might be all consuming for a while it is important to remember that you are still an individual with your own interests, needs and dreams.

I try to get out of the house as much as possible. I've noticed that the days that I am home with bub all day (by myself) — those are the hardest days. I've also noticed that the days we have playgroup or play dates or a picnic with friends are the best days of the week.

PREGNANCY — THE PHYSICAL AND EMOTIONAL CHALLENGES

There are many different reactions to the confirmation of pregnancy and they all depend on your personal circumstances. They might include negative feelings (such as shock, distress, anger, fear and/or feeling overwhelmed) or positive feelings (such as relief, excitement, anticipation and/or feeling very special and precious). Some women feel no particular emotional response at all.

There is not just one way we should feel when we find out we are pregnant. These are all valid feelings and may well change over the course of the pregnancy: pregnancies don't always go according to plan. Some women love being pregnant and others find it a significant physical struggle and challenge. Everybodies' experiences are uniquely their own and you shouldn't feel that you ought be feeling a particular way.

Caring for yourself during pregnancy

Some women love being pregnant, others hate it. Be realistic, feeling tired, emotional and sick during those first few months is very common. It is also common to have a different emotional response to each pregnancy. Don't feel bad if you don't feel good. Some women will enjoy the second trimester only to struggle again later in the pregnancy as they become heavy and uncomfortable. Some women glow and feel healthy, while others feel sick for nine months. Some pregnancies are complicated, others are straightforward. Being pregnant whilst looking after your other children is just plain physically demanding.

Most women enjoy maintaining their activities throughout pregnancy, sometimes with modifications. Keeping fit and active is also good for the soul (perhaps not running marathons or abseiling) and this often means keeping regular contact with friends. Other women find that pregnancy is an excellent excuse to start getting a bit more active and join exercise classes specifically designed for pregnant women such as aqua aerobics. These classes can present great opportunities to develop long-lasting friendships.

Pregnancy might also be the first time you really think about looking after yourself. Don't feel you have to do everything. This might also be a time of reflection and slowing down. Some couples take the opportunity to have one last holiday before the arrival of the baby.

Your pregnancy experience is unique, so don't compare yourself with others and don't judge others. Don't think you 'should' be enjoying yourself. Remember that around 10% of pregnant women experience antenatal depression and/or anxiety — one out of ten women — and many others have mixed feelings during this time. Pregnancy can be a time when many feelings surface, perhaps related to past relationships, relationships with your parents, past pregnancies or past pregnancy losses. Finding a trusted person to speak with about your feelings can perhaps help you move into a more positive frame of mind. However, if you just love being pregnant, then that's great.

MANAGING FEELINGS ABOUT THE BIRTH

Debriefing after the birth is really important and doesn't always occur. The birth may have been a mind blowing, amazing, empowering experience or it may have left you feeling deflated. Perhaps you accepted the drugs you vowed you wouldn't or didn't get the drugs you were promised. You may have put a lot of thought into a birth plan that was dismissed by your caregivers. Sometimes the baby differs in some way from the dream, perhaps being premature or disabled, perhaps not being the sex that was anticipated.

Perceptions of the birth experience can cause distress for some mothers. In the case of one of the authors this led to a debilitating posttraumatic stress disorder. It is really important for many mothers (and some fathers) to be given the opportunity to process their feelings about the birth. Many mothers need this opportunity to reframe expectations and refocus their thoughts. A professional who will listen can make a huge difference.

CONSIDER POSTTRAUMATIC STRESS DISORDER (PTSD)

This anxiety disorder is thought to be much more prevalent than previously recognised. It is often not discussed by women who may find it difficult to articulate exactly how they are feeling. PTSD might be triggered through a traumatic birth experience, or other traumatic aspects of your life might resurface such as childhood trauma, pregnancy loss (including terminations) and unplanned pregnancies. PTSD can manifest as intrusive and repetitive thoughts which can be quite debilitating and might include flashbacks to the birth or other past traumatic experiences. Professional counselling can be very successful in treating PTSD. One treatment which is currently popular is called eye movement desensitisation and reprocessing (EMDR). See www.emdrhap.org for trials, studies and information. Also *beyondblue: A guide to what works for anxiety disorders,* **www.mhfa.com.au/documents/whatworks_ anxietydisorders.pdf**

MANAGING THE EARLY MONTHS OF MOTHERHOOD AND BEYOND

Interacting with other parents is truly my saving grace. Knowing there are lots of other mums going through what I'm going through is hugely encouraging and keeps me sane.

All women will have expectations of motherhood drawn from cultural backgrounds, the media and personal experiences, including those from childhood. Keeping an open mind and a flexible approach can be very helpful when you have a new baby and young children. None of us really know what to expect and each baby is different. As a new mother it is also very easy to get caught up in the media hype surrounding motherhood and perfection. All of us need to learn to view anything we see in the media with a healthy scepticism... we live in the real world.

Maintaining good self-esteem helps new mothers to be dismissive of unhelpful thoughts. Self-awareness, acknowledging the type of person you are, your strengths and weaknesses, triggers that might set you off, and your comfort zone helps to support your self-esteem. And remember, your perceptions may be distorted by your own unhelpful thoughts.

PRACTICAL IDEAS FOR TODAY, TOMORROW AND INTO THE FUTURE

Exercise, time alone, being in a book club, working, giving back to others and not expecting myself to be all things to all people all of the time. Sometimes I forget this!

I work two to three days a week. I go to the gym a couple of times a week (ideally) and I have five hours a week to myself and the house when they are at preschool.

Mothers, fathers and families exist in a nebulous, constantly evolving and frequently changing universe. Hopefully, the following ideas will provide food for thought — some may be relevant today, others may be more helpful in the future. We hope they underline the notion that mothering changes day-by-day, year-by-year, and that this gives hope to mothers who may feel that they are 'stuck'.

To begin with:
- Accept that for the first few months you may feel overwhelming tiredness. This will change. Remind yourself that life always

seems more overwhelming when you are tired, but it is just a perception.

- As babies grow their needs change, as do yours. Babies do not have routines and this is normal. Try to be flexible.
- When you feel totally overwhelmed just live one day at a time.
- Accept that you don't have the same time and energy to give to your partner and that the time you spend together will be different. As your baby grows you will have more time, both as a couple, and together as a family.
- Find time just to 'be' with your baby. Getting to know your baby, interacting with her, watching her reactions, talking or singing to her, even dancing with her can make you feel good too.
- If your baby is unsettled and that is distressing for you, lie your baby safely in his cot and leave the room — go out of earshot — for a few minutes.
- Find time for fun, either with your baby, your partner, or with other friends or family. A good sense of the ridiculous can be very healthy. If fun is elusive, perhaps that is an indication that you could do with some emotional support, or at least a friend to talk to.
- Try to articulate your feelings to your partner. If your partner can understand where you are coming from this will help the two of you to form a united front. It is much easier to deal with the world from a position of strength. A partner who is emotionally supportive can also help to manage difficult friends and family.
- Surround yourself with people who make you feel good about yourself. Positive, sensitive, light-hearted, non-judgemental friends are incredibly valuable, as are friends with initiative. Some people can offer simple practical help. Other friends can offer invaluable emotional support.
- Accept the help you are offered, whatever the form: a meal, babysitting, shopping, cleaning or tidying, the list is endless. And don't be afraid to ask for help.

As the months go by:

- If you are feeling particularly fragile, join a specific postnatal depression group. While these groups offer support and counselling they also enable mothers to mix with each other in a non-judgemental environment. They also provide opportunity for friendships to develop.
- Continue your appointments with health professionals: doctors, counsellors and/or the early childhood nurse. If you are really unwell you will need support from friends and family to enable you to do this. Maintaining regular appointments will help with your recovery.
- Both parents should try to arm themselves with knowledge about perinatal anxiety and depression. Friends and family are bound to ask you questions and will sometimes make unhelpful comments. A bit of knowledge can put you in a position of strength, and help to counter those pesky 'why don't you just snap out of it' comments.

As time moves on:

- Take your toddlers and preschoolers on simple outings with other friends or adult family members. It can be fun to enjoy outings with other adults.
- If you find those witching hours too horrible to bear enlist the help of friends or family (with or without children). Feeding children en masse and early, then putting them all in the bath together can be very therapeutic for everyone concerned. A regular weekly dinner and bath date with another family can provide a structured activity that you can look forward to. Having a friend drop in from time to time and help with the evening chaos is also great. The company of another adult can help to make this time bearable.
- The sky will not fall in if you have a BBQ chicken or Thai takeaway every so often.
- Put some structure into your life. Organise some regular enjoyable activities with positive friends and family (but don't overdo it!). This might include a weekly coffee

morning, or a children's play afternoon. It might involve a regular tennis morning with a babysitter for all the children, or a gym commitment, or perhaps an evening at the movies. Some mothers form book clubs, others create 'dinner groups' with their partners. Some organise a regular subscription to the local theatre. Feeling connected to a community is very important and you can make lifelong friends with regular activities continuing for years.

- Work outside the home is an issue that many mothers need to confront at some point. There are many variables, positive and negative, depending on each family's situation.

- Parents need to find time for themselves. This might be a few hours to read a book or indulge in a hobby (maybe to pursue a physical activity or perhaps music, painting or scrapbooking etc) or even go to the hairdresser. Some mothers enjoy doing some volunteer work during this time, others find fulfilment in doing a part-time course which might be for enjoyment or perhaps to improve future employment prospects.

- Mothers and fathers also need to find time to spend together. Time, communication and intimacy, these are important. Couples need to nurture their own relationship if it is to remain strong and meaningful.

- Women suffering from perinatal anxiety and/or depression do get better. However, recovery can take months and everyone involved needs to appreciate that there will be ups and downs along the way. Accessing help is the start, but the journey can be very frustrating, especially if people anticipate immediate results. Be prepared for the long haul, but keep in mind that women (and men) do recover from this, and go on to enjoy their lives and their families.

- Write lists, particularly if you are feeling overwhelmed. The lists don't just have to be for yourself, they can help others who may be helping you. Crossing off items on the list can give you a sense of achievement. Don't make lists so long they are self defeating. Work out what you need to do to get by and don't try to do too much. In addition, lists don't just have to be filled with practical 'to do' items. You might like to write a list of hopes and dreams for the future. Take some time to think about where you would like to be and what you would like to be doing in 12 months, 2 years... and so on.

And into the future:

- Invest in a recipe book that will provide you with inspiration for children and adults. Trying to be creative with food night after night, year after year can be very challenging. You may like to cook with your partner or your partner may enjoy cooking.

- Babies do grow up, they change and develop. One day your baby will be leaving home and you will be nostalgically yearning for these innocent early childhood days. If you are finding some aspects of this time difficult remind yourself that it is just one part of the journey. We all manage different aspects of parenting differently. Some mothers just love little newborn babies, others enjoy parenting their one and two year olds more. If you feel you are stuck in a surreal 'groundhog day' try to be pragmatic. Time marches on and the issues you are dealing with next month will be very different.

- Remind yourself that 'mother', while the most important, is not the only role you play. You are still an individual with interests, activities, hopes and dreams.

THE WAY YOU THINK WILL AFFECT THE WAY YOU FEEL

Here are some ideas to help you negotiate your way through the thoughts you may have during this time... particularly in the early hours of the morning... and throughout your life.

- Lots of other mothers with babies will also be awake at this time, feeding or trying to settle their baby — you are part of a vast community of middle-of-the-night mothers. Some mothers go online in the early hours and connect with their virtual community.

- This is a new chapter in your life — give yourself time to re-adjust.
- Don't be hard on yourself.
- Don't expect perfection.
- It is ok to be sad sometimes. Sadness is a natural human emotion and so is anxiety. There is only a problem if you are feeling consumed by these emotions all the time, if there is no joy at all in your life.
- It's ok to grieve the loss of your old life, while at the same time realising that this can also be a period of personal growth, and the start of a whole new adventure.
- Take time to consider some of the positives in your life, even if they are very simple:
  - I like to go for a walk with my baby on a sunny day.
  - I like to sit and hold my baby when he is calm.
  - I love watching my baby sleep.
  - I really enjoy meeting up with my friends for coffee.
- Be mindful of the situations you find stressful (so you can prepare yourself for them):
  - I get tense when my baby cries incessantly for no apparent reason.
  - One particular friend always leaves me feeling unsettled.
  - My mother-in-law always makes me feel so inadequate.
- Develop self-awareness. Get to know yourself and the things that make you feel good, along with the triggers that might set you off.

Congratulate yourself on the small achievements and remind yourself that there are certain situations that would upset lots of people. Try to be insightful and realistic.

SINGLE MOTHERS AND ISOLATED MOTHERS

Pregnancy and motherhood throw up an additional set of issues for women who find themselves on their own. A helpful family or a group of supportive friends can make all the difference if you are in this situation. You may also be lucky enough to connect with other mothers at the early childhood centre.

It is really important that you and the people around you acknowledge that what you are doing is hard work, both physically and emotionally.

> *Both sets of grandparents were interstate and any friends that I had were busy with their own children. Eventually I employed a wonderful nanny/helper who would assist me with the four children and she saved my life!*

WHEN YOU FEEL YOU ARE LOSING CONTROL OF YOUR EMOTIONAL SELF

Positive ways of thinking are all very well if you are feeling ok some of the time. If your mood is very low or if you are feeling highly anxious however, it is virtually impossible to use these sorts of techniques without the support of a health professional.

A relationship with a health professional (whether counsellor, psychologist or psychiatrist) is important to maintain. There might also be times when medication is appropriate.

If people tell you to 'snap out of it' you must remind yourself that you are suffering from a diagnosable illness. If you had a broken leg you wouldn't be told to just get up and start walking on it. The sympathetic advice from all around you would be to 'take care of yourself so your leg has time to heal'. The same should be said when you are suffering from anxiety and/or depression. Unfortunately, however, it is more often the case in our society that issues of mental illness do not illicit the same response.

Mothers suffering from perinatal mood disorders also need time to heal. This may involve ongoing counselling, sometimes medication, and possible admission to a mother-baby unit where there are specialised staff. Unfortunately, these units are only located in capital cities, are usually small and there are very few that cater for public patients. Yet for women who are very unwell these units provide the sanctuary they need. During this time their mood can be stabilised through careful administration of medication and they have access to counselling and practical help.

ACCESSING PROFESSIONAL HELP

A professional perspective for those struggling to adapt:

> *I tend to work in a cognitive behavioural framework and use very straightforward techniques. My strategies include getting mums to connect with other mums via a mothers' group or playgroup. I also encourage them to spend time with other friends with kids. Other strategies include exercise, as this has been shown to lift depression and a low mood. I think it's very important for mums to consider their self-care and take time out regularly for themselves. Getting as much sleep as possible is also crucial. It can change the whole dynamic of the family when everyone is sleep deprived. (health professional)*

Professional help may involve:

- **Talking therapy** — can help you to change unhelpful thinking patterns. The way we feel is often a reflection of how we are thinking about the world. Learning to challenge negative thoughts can be very empowering. Three main types of talking therapies are used to help mothers (and fathers) in dealing with perinatal anxiety and depression: cognitive behaviour therapy (CBT), interpersonal therapy and mindfulness (see Chapter 6 for more detailed information).

• **Medication** — prescribed and monitored by a GP or psychiatrist can play an important role in assisting with the wellbeing and recovery of mothers struggling with a perinatal mood disorder (see Chapter 7 for more detailed information).

The help I received from my counsellor has remained with me as my children have grown up. I learnt a lot about myself. I came to recognise the things that make me stressed and what makes me feel good. I've learnt to manage my own life better which has meant I've been a stronger mother for my children. This helped me to deal with personal and family difficulties at other times in my life.

My partner and I went to the psychologist together. She helped me to understand what my partner was going through and how my actions could influence the situation — positively or negatively. The strategies I learnt then have stayed with me, and helped many times over the years. I think my relationship with my partner and my children has benefited from the help we both received all those years ago.

I gained insight and awareness through my sessions with a psychologist. I understand that in order to be a confident wife and mother I need to look after myself.

SUPPORT, RELATIONSHIPS, SUPPORT!

Whether from family, friends or professionals, whether it is in a practical or emotional form, support is what is important. Don't parent in isolation. If you are struggling in any way, the sooner you reach out for help, from friends or professionals, the sooner you will start to feel better. You, your partner and your children will benefit both now and in the future.

Strong families need healthy parents who have the capacity to care for and nurture their children from the time they are born through to adulthood. Caring for a family within the context of a community provides us all with support and outlets. Caring for ourselves is important if we are to be good carers for our partners and children. Finding our own balance in our own lives is really important. Understanding ourselves and what makes us tick gives us the capacity to be understanding parents to our children.

15
START TALKING

Surely women don't need any encouragement to 'start talking' you must be thinking. There is certainly plenty of unflattering folklore relating to women and talking. It therefore seems quite counterintuitive that women need to be encouraged to talk. Yet, in relation to feelings and experiences of pregnancy and parenting there is a great need for both women and men to be encouraged to talk... honestly.

On becoming parents we become members of a not particularly elite club. By default, this club counts as its members most of humanity. Yet the initiation rights to the club seem to involve a cone of silence. We may well know mothers capable of speaking under water, and we might all think that we share the mysteries of 'secret mothers business', but how often do we really have a truthful conversation with each other?

As soon as mothers feel supported and are given permission to talk honestly... they do, as you can see by the following comments from some of our contributors.

I try to casually mention that I think I had postnatal depression or anxiety when mixing with other women — it sometimes helps open them up and encourage talking.

We need to make some huge changes to how we all talk about kids and families in this country. Get over the rose-tinted glasses thing and realise that having a family is hard work, as well as a lovely thing.

It's harder when families are so scattered these days and so there's less chance of people seeing their aunties and cousins and older siblings becoming parents. I think that's a real problem. Our local community can, and needs to, fill the gap that our smaller, modern families have caused.

Everything needs to improve and to change. First and foremost, women need to support other women rather than falling into the trap of competing with one another.

So, what is the secret to parental honesty? What happens if parents want a refund on their club membership because they think it is not providing them with the benefits they anticipated? Because of this conspiracy of silence many of us spend our lives 'keeping up appearances' and maintaining a picture-perfect public image while behind the smile there is a lot of struggling going on. We authors, and many of our contributors, certainly showed great talent in hiding the truth. We were faultless club members, appearing to perform the role of immaculate motherhood to perfection.

SO, WE CAN START HERE BY SHARING SOME TRUTHS…

Mothering needs to be acknowledged as an important BUT very difficult and labour-intensive job and there needs to be much greater integration of services: antenatal to childbirth and on to the postnatal period.

I think there is a 'conspiracy of silence' whereby motherhood is made out to be the ultimate fulfilment. Yet no-one tells you when you're pregnant about the hard work to come. There are also lots of myths around, particularly that you will 'fall in love' with your baby immediately and feel euphoric after the birth and so on. This is more often than not a load of rubbish!!

Many women spend pregnancy in the limelight. It is actually 'all about them' with doctors, midwives, partners and friends showering them with attention. Despite pregnancy discomforts many women do 'bloom'. This attention reaches its peak during the birth and for a few days following.

Then, in our society, the mother goes home, often her partner returns to work and she is left with a newborn baby. There can be limited social interaction, sleep deprivation and an overwhelming sense of responsibility to care for her baby. Breastfeeding may be difficult. She may be sore as a result of the birth. She then discovers that our society does not value motherhood as purposeful and she may find herself isolated and alone.

Our society needs a better system of aftercare for all mothers in the early stages of their baby's life. Early childhood nurses need funding and resources and backup. Women need to feel supported as part of a community of new mothers.

Motherhood can indeed be wonderful. The exquisite love we feel for our babies and children is quite extraordinary. The experiences we can have as parents with our children can be funny, even hilarious, lovely and precious. Yet, this is only part of the story. We need to talk about the whole picture: the long nights without sleep, the days when we're not sure if we even like our children, and the days their messy presence, constant crying and/or bickering just doesn't let up and we are pushed to the edge.

Instead of recognising that words such as 'relentless' or 'resilience' can be used in connection with motherhood, women are often expected to describe their experiences as 'beautiful', 'perfect', 'wonderful', 'natural', 'the ultimate experience' and 'all I ever dreamed of'.

The reality is that there are times when being a mother to babies and young children is emotionally and physically draining and above all challenging. Yet, no-one wants to be the first to admit this. While significant anxiety and/or depression is experienced by 16% of mothers (and 10% of fathers) it is widely believed that many more parents experience different forms of distress during the early weeks and months of caring for a new baby. Until very recently the challenges faced by many parents have been largely overlooked.

You can see the pressure on women regarding birthing and breastfeeding. Women want the best for their babies and are very aware of falling short of societal expectations.

I always try to emphasise to friends that it's ok to find it hard and it's ok to feel ambivalent towards your children. Some days they will just annoy you, some days you will feel as if it's all been a horrible mistake. But if we all know a bit more about that, and learn to be resilient... that'll help!!

Motherhood needs to be valued more. Mothers need better practical and emotional care after birth. We see cases all the time where women give birth, then go home and have no support network. This is terrible, and a sad sign of how our communities are lacking. I feel mothers need to be nurtured themselves especially in the first months, but popular culture portrays a myth which can make women feel inadequate.

Fathers need permission to speak honestly too. While the simple fact of biology places mothers on centre stage during this period, most fathers are also emotionally engaged. Their struggles, while different, can't be ignored.

WHY WE DON'T TALK

The last quotation sums it up beautifully. Throughout our lives we are drip fed a romantic fairy tale. When the reality of pregnancy and early parenting hits us it brings with it culture shock and more often than not an identity crisis. This may then be coupled with performance anxiety as we attempt to perform our role as 'mother'. The final blow is the deafening silence from other mothers around us. Many of us therefore continue to live our parallel lives under our personal cones of silence.

Over the last ten years or so a number of authors have examined the paradoxes of contemporary motherhood. Many of these writers have exposed a number of myths and cultural norms which are not necessarily helpful to mothers or fathers. They seem to paint a rather opaque picture of motherhood. It is often difficult for mothers to really get a handle on what is happening in their lives, let alone talk about it, when truth and reality are twisted around socially accepted myths.

Conflicting perspectives in the paradise of motherhood

Susan Maushart in her book *The Mask of Motherhood*, includes a list of places where she sees the Mask of Motherhood operating. It is a list we feel many of you will relate to. We would like to include our own list here which is a mixture of some of the issues highlighted in *The Mask of Motherhood* along with other ideas that have come from discussions with our many contributors.

This mask hides the truth for those of us who have sat at a new mothers' group with a big smile on our face, lying to the world that everything is great or who have desperately tried to appear calm and in control in the supermarket as our toddler rampages around while our baby screams.

- Motherhood is romanticised yet at the same time many

mothers feel invisible.

- Commentators would have us believe that motherhood is the most important job in the world yet many mothers feel their busy days are undervalued.
- Glossy magazines portray celebrity motherhood as something we should all be able to manage, which of course makes most of us feel silently inadequate.
- Parenting magazines explore the high achieving lives of supposedly ordinary mothers leaving the rest of us feeling even more inadequate.
- Some self help books make us feel like slouches for not following strict diets and fitness regimes designed to create the new 'yummy mummy body' in weeks.
- Books and magazines which describe motherhood in idealised terms, such as 'natural', send us messages that we should all aspire to being a 'natural' mother lest we be seen as 'failures'.
- Parenting books that outline 'foolproof' ways to parent that don't seem to work for our babies: for example, even if we follow their instructions to the letter, our babies still do not sleep through the night leaving us with that 'failure' feeling once again.
- Breastfeeding agendas which do not allow for the variations in our bodies and our lives which might lead to different feeding outcomes.
- Doing 'what's best for baby' when in fact 'what's best for the family' should be considered.
- Judgemental perspectives on mothers who work outside the home and then judgemental perspectives on mothers whose lives are focused inside the home are both destructive.

This list could go on and on now that it's started. It's important for us all to remember that 'appearances can be deceiving'. It's especially important for us to remember this when we are feeling emotionally fragile, anxious or depressed.

Here are some reasons why mothers and fathers find it difficult to start talking:

I think I am the only one who is feeling like this

It is very difficult to start a conversation about your feelings if you think that you are the only one who is not on the same page as everyone else. It is a very lonely place to be and thus women who feel this way will often tend to keep their thoughts and feelings to themselves. The irony is of course that if everyone did talk they would realise that lots of other women are also on that very same page.

I am confused about how I really feel

Conversations are also hard to initiate if you are not really sure how you feel. Many parents find that they are in such shock for the first weeks or months, that simply getting through each day is a significant physical effort. It will come as no surprise then to hear that these new parents can be confused about their feelings. Self-awareness is a wonderful thing, if you have the time to consider it.

I don't want to share my vulnerability with the world

And that's ok too. Soul bearing is not imperative. Indeed, talking about your deepest thoughts with all and sundry can be counterproductive.

Many of us have high expectations of ourselves as mothers, yet the realities of motherhood can leave us feeling inadequate. To admit that we are finding motherhood challenging can appear to be a sign of failure. It is sometimes easier to hide behind the created image of the successful mother than to let down our defences and show what is really happening.

No-one is giving me the opportunity to really talk

Visits to health professionals, outings with friends, days at work may all be peopled with individuals that you communicate with, except that you might not really talk to them and they might not be really listening to you. We are all familiar with the following one-sided exchange 'How are you?', 'Good?', 'That's great!' There's no opportunity for you to respond: 'Actually I feel awful'. Proper talking may also not occur during regular appointments with your doctor or midwife because you might feel too embarrassed, too hurried or you might simply forget what you wanted to say. Sometimes it's as simple as not being asked how you really feel and not having the strength to initiate the conversation without that question.

People may not understand what I am saying

Some women feel they muster the courage to finally bare their soul to someone only to receive an indifferent response, or even worse, an admonishment. When you leave yourself emotionally exposed you really want someone to listen properly and to try to understand where you are coming from. It is understandable that this fear causes some parents to think the best strategy is to say nothing.

IF WE DO START TALKING WE MIGHT START A SCARE CAMPAIGN...

There is a common saying that 'knowledge is power', and we think that many mothers would agree with this sentiment. It's certainly the case during pregnancy. Most prospective first time parents will attend some form of antenatal education. A class full of individuals all anticipating a new adventure into parenthood will receive plenty of information on the physicality of pregnancy and birth. This can also be a perfect location to start a discussion about the feelings surrounding pregnancy and parenting.

The baby outcome at the end of the pregnancy can be the elephant in the room. Antenatal education provides us with amazing insights into the extraordinary things that our bodies will be expected to do. The focus of course is on 'The Birth'. (To be perfectly honest, what pregnant mother doesn't feel slightly stressed, maybe even obsessed, with wondering how this baby, which just keeps getting bigger, is ever going to get out?) Every aspect of this process is dissected, with parents becoming authorities on cervical dilation, birth plans, birth options, birthing positions, drugs and even suggestions for support people. Yet childbirth is not the culmination of the pregnancy, parenthood is. Unfortunately this little gem of information can sometimes get lost in all attention focused on 'The Birth'.

What about 'The Baby' then? After all, 'The Birth' might well have been a 24-hour marathon, but 'The Baby' is going to be an addition to your life forever.

Antenatal classes are a perfect opportunity for parents to start talking about how the arrival of a third person might change the family dynamic. Traditionally, antenatal classes did not really cover early parenting issues and thus is could actually be very hard for pregnant mothers and their partners to really conceptualise what life would be like with their new baby. However, over the last few years antenatal educators have been including more information on what new parents might expect to encounter during those jumbled first few weeks and months with a new baby.

While there is some truth in the notion that there are pregnant women who can't focus on anything beyond the birth, pregnancy is a wonderful time for women to contemplate motherhood. There is a real need for couples to look beyond the pregnancy and process of birth in order to give some space to consider the end product — the child. One obstetrician we spoke to is constantly bemused by the regular surprised exclamation by so many couples after that last push: 'Look ... It's a baby!' What were they expecting?

Spending some time during antenatal classes on issues of early parenting allows couples the opportunity to start talking about their expectations. In a nonjudgemental environment the educator can discuss some of the common myths and well known issues confronting new parents. A dose of reality at this stage might well help some parents to avoid some of the shock that accompanies the arrival of a new baby.

There are a number of resources that educators use to help get prospective parents to start talking. One powerful tool is having a couple with a young baby come and talk about their experiences. There is also an educational and informative DVD which is available for use in antenatal (as well as postnatal) parenting classes. Called 'Behind the Mask: The Hidden Struggle of Parenthood', this DVD includes the voices of parents and health professionals reflecting on the emotional journey that so many of us have taken. Divided into a number of short eight-minute segments, each one focusing on a different aspect of pregnancy or parenthood, the structure of the DVD enables a group of parents to watch one or two segments and then discuss their responses to the content. (See the Gidget Foundation entry in the Resources Guide at the back of this book.)

It is encouraging to see that there are a number of positive attempts being made by various health professionals and educators to enable parents to start talking during the months before the baby arrives. This must help to alleviate some of the disjuncture between expectation and reality. The importance of these discussions is also reflected in the comments of some of our contributors:

We need more parenting help, including in antenatal classes, and more follow-up by health professionals. At the moment if you need more help the onus is on you and your family to seek it.

There should be more emphasis on psychological changes and wellbeing in antenatal classes. Parenthood needs to be seen as valuable and families need to be supported in this transition. Antenatal education should include more information about the transition to parenthood.

Women need to be educated and informed in the antenatal period by their GPs and obstetric and midwifery carers about the existence of antenatal and postnatal depression so that warning signs can be identified and early intervention initiated, and prompt and effective treatment and support can be provided.

Women need to be encouraged to stop having such high expectations of themselves — they are setting themselves up to fail. More antenatal education relating to emotional issues, not just the birth, is needed. More postnatal support relating to

feelings and issues rather than just physical support/looking after the baby would be helpful.

Antenatal classes have been a bonus for expectant parents over the last couple of generations. Apart from providing practical information they have also helped to initiate conversations which have challenged some birth conventions and led to changes, usually for the better. The classes can also provide a perfect opportunity for supported conversations about parenting. After all, realistic information on childbirth has not stopped women getting pregnant and having babies. Rather, many women now feel more empowered with the birth choices that they make. Access to education and reliable information has changed the way many women and men approach pregnancy and childbirth.

If parents are encouraged to start talking about their emotional journeys through pregnancy and their expectations of parenthood they might have the opportunity to get their heads around some of the inevitable changes that will take place. They might be more prepared for the possibility of anxiety and/or depression. What better environment to do this than in a supportive antenatal class with a trained facilitator: perhaps forewarned really is forearmed. More importantly, however, providing information will raise awareness of what to expect — overwhelming love and overwhelming exhaustion, feelings of elation and feelings of despair. Let's tell the whole story.

IS IT POSSIBLE TO START TALKING TO MY MIDWIFE, GP OR OBSTETRICIAN?

I think where the change needs to take place is within the medical profession so that doctors, nurses, psychologists, psychiatrists and maternal and child health nurses have MUCH more of an understanding of postnatal depression. I have heard of MANY GPs who are absolutely NOT helpful. I think they just don't understand or don't have the experience.

In my experience, there are some health professionals who really don't know the resources in the postnatal depression area and some who really shouldn't be working in the area!

I noticed when I had my second child that depression and anxiety were now being screened for antenatally. There were also more psychologists attached to maternity hospitals so improvements are slowly happening. I think GP's should have more education about postnatal depression and anxiety, especially the male doctors!

Most women will receive antenatal care from a midwife, GP or obstetrician, and often a combination of the three. These health professionals all care about the emotional wellbeing of you as their patient, yet they may not necessarily ask you questions about your mood. If however, you would like to talk about your emotional health you will find that most midwives and doctors will be very open to having this discussion.

In most cases your antenatal caregiver would like to know how you are feeling. If you're not being asked the right questions, and you find it difficult to raise the subject, write down a list of what you would like to talk about and take it along to your next visit. When making the appointment to see your doctor ask for a double appointment so there is time to talk properly. This will also give the doctor an indication that there is more to this visit than a regular check-up. Issues surrounding emotional health are often more complex and time consuming to deal with than those related to your physical health. Generally speaking, your midwife or doctor is in a position to help you in all sorts of ways if they know how you are really feeling.

Talking about your emotional wellbeing can take a huge amount of effort but we all know from experience how important this conversation is. So, when things are worrying you, take a deep breath and take the plunge. If your caregiver doesn't know how you are feeling they are not in a position to help you. And if their response is less than helpful, perhaps they are not the right person to be caring for you.

There is another opportunity to start talking which is available to some women. Relatively recently antenatal mental health screening has begun in a number of public maternity hospitals across the country (see Chapter 4 for more information). This screening interview does give mothers an excellent opportunity to start talking. The environment created by the midwife in this situation allows a mother to voice the concerns she may be having while she is pregnant and to consider how she might feel after the baby is born. Use this opportunity to start talking.

As you can imagine, mothers have also begun talking to each other about this interview. In some cases it has become a conversation starter. Many women are curious to know what their friends talked to the midwife about, what questions were asked, what answers given. Let's hope this leads to some honest conversations and stronger, deeper bonds of friendships. Let's have less competition, more compassion.

Through talking to a professional you will hopefully receive a greater level of support. You might even be referred to a counsellor or perhaps a support group where shared stories help us all to realise we are not alone. Professionals should have the capacity to listen and provide assistance. Yet, we do sound a note of caution: beware of conflicting authoritative advice. There is still a need for improvement in this area of professional help.

We need much closer alliance between the medical (obstetricians) and the psychological service providers. I fell between the gaps.

If there was someone, for example, a child health nurse/ counsellor/GP assigned to follow up each family that would be good. They would just need to make contact and see how the family is going and encourage them or help them to seek the appropriate help if it is needed. I think many people would

*benefit, especially those who say 'I think I can manage it on
my own' but who really can't.*

*Also it would help those people that are just so down that they
don't have the energy to get the help themselves. I realise that
this is probably unrealistic with the already stretched health
workers, but it would be helpful.*

beyondblue has recently launched a new initiative and website:
www.justspeakup.com.au. Here you will find many personal stories
from ordinary people as well as helpful information.

Health care professionals also need help to start talking. There
is still very little information on perinatal anxiety and depression
included in most of the medical and nursing training in Australia.
While this is changing slowly, there are still many health professionals
who feel ill-equipped to help families who are struggling along
during pregnancy and into early parenthood. As a result many
professionals don't start talking with patients. Many health
professionals do obtain whatever information they can through
'inservice' courses, workshops, meetings or conferences. However,
accessing information on mental health during the perinatal period
is still very reliant on the interest and drive of each individual health
professional.

START TALKING TO YOUR PARTNER AND YOUR PARTNER MIGHT START TALKING TOO

Men and women are generally in this together. But here's the thing,
according to gender stereotyping, women like to talk while men
like to be strong and silent. Is this the truth or just another myth
that needs to be shattered? If mothers are finding pregnancy and
parenting confusing, how must fathers be feeling. Contrary to
stereotyping most men don't want to spend all their time down at the

pub with their mates... many actually do want a good relationship with their partner and their children. Communication is the key.

The arrival of a baby puts a lot of additional strain on a relationship. Finding time to talk to your partner helps them to understand what you are really feeling. Expressing your exhaustion is one thing, but dealing with anxiety and depression takes the need for an understanding partner to an entirely new level.

Mothering small babies can feel claustrophobic for some women: their world narrows and they can feel diminished. Intimacy is often a casualty of a new baby. The ability to talk to your partner when all else seems lost is a real gift.

Blokes also need to talk to blokes (see Chapter 9). They might talk at the pub, or at the footy, on the golf course, even on a blokes' only camping trip. Wherever and whenever the talking happens, other fathers can be a great source of strength.

START TALKING TO YOUR FAMILY

Most women find that their greatest support during this time will probably come from their partner or their close family. Through talking to their families women can help those closest to them to understand more about the challenges mothers face when living with perinatal anxiety and depression. Communicating with family members helps them to appreciate that the road to recovery can be long and bumpy, full of unexpected challenges.

Because of my dad and his clinical experience, I was directed to help quickly (within 12 days after the arrival of my daughter). We were like rabbits caught in the head lights and we had no idea what was happening to us: the changes in our relationship, learning to look after a new being, the sleep deprivation etc, and people telling us over and over again that what we were experiencing was just normal adjustment. If it were not for my dad and his early intervention, I would have ended up in a

*mother and baby unit with a long recovery ahead of me. I
realise that not everyone has a dad who is a specialist in the
area, however I think there needs to be much greater education
for those people who are involved in the care of mothers and
babies — education and recognition of the symptoms so they
can direct mothers to help quickly.*

Starting the conversation might be difficult, but try explaining in
terms of your health and your real need for some extra help. Most
families will try and be supportive even if at first they don't fully
understand. Asking for practical help is a starting point, and you
will generally find that emotional support will follow.

START TALKING TO FRIENDS

Talking to friends is also essential, but it is important to choose
carefully which friends, when you want to talk, and how much you
want to tell them. Concentrate on the friends who make you feel
good. When you are feeling fragile and angry and on edge you do
not need friends who think they can 'fix' you. You might not want
to talk to some friends straight away. Leave the talking to more
challenging friends until you are feeling stronger.

*I bring it up all the time amongst friends and family. Just the
other day postnatal depression was front page news in our local
paper because the numbers suggest cases in our area are double
the rate of other areas. Well I flashed that newspaper around,
people need to realise just how horrific and real this illness is
and that it is happening all around us.*

You may find that it is friends who provide you with the best
support. Their emotional investment in you is very different to
that of your family. Being slightly removed from your immediate
situation might also help them see things a bit differently.

START TALKING IN THE WORKPLACE

Both men and women in the workplace benefit from a shared knowledge of the difficulties of parenting. From experience in presenting talks on perinatal anxiety and depression to various workplaces we know that a straightforward half-hour presentation is enough to start the conversations and questions. Interestingly, it is often fathers who are inclined to ask the most questions.

Talking in the workplace not only provides insight into anxiety and depression around pregnancy, it also brings the more common struggles of parenting into a community forum. Many working people are also parents, and this needs to be acknowledged.

HOW CAN WE START TALKING AS A COMMUNITY?

As a community we need to learn to listen too.

Education, media exposure, we need to talk about postnatal depression. So many cases go undiagnosed as I believe women feel pressured into staying silent and suffering alone.

I do raise the subject sometimes when I can, especially if I have a good relationship with someone whom I believe to be at risk. I think a caring attitude helps with someone who has postnatal depression and/or anxiety. Asking 'how are you?' or 'are you really ok?' — in other words, paying close attention — may help them talk to you.

Starting a conversation with a new parent can often open the floodgates. While this may be confronting it can also be very therapeutic. Most importantly, it helps to raise awareness of the challenges of parenting in the community. It is also a way to reduce the stigma attached to perinatal anxiety and depression.

Learning to listen to new parents is very important, as is asking the right questions.

We all should learn to be aware of:
- body language and facial expressions
- not interrupting, just listening
- avoiding the temptation to express an 'I'll see you and raise you' reaction — ie my crisis is worse than yours
- concentrating — try not to get distracted
- not being judgemental
- feeling we have to provide feedback or answers. Sometimes a hug is all that is needed.

WHY IS IT GOOD TO START TALKING?

We all share a common humanity. It is comforting to know that other parents have similar experiences to our own. All of us feel relief when we hear of others' struggles with parenting; not because we wish them ill, rather, because of our shared humanity.

I am very open about my having had postnatal depression and don't hide it from people. I talk about it a fair bit at my mothers' group, now that I know the ladies well. I try to correct myths about postnatal depression when people make uninformed comments (which is often!)

There is also a lot of stigma attached to mental health issues and postnatal depression in particular, as people tend to associate it with the high-profile cases in the media of babies being harmed and so on. I would say the majority of women with postnatal depression are not at risk of harming themselves or their child, but they do need support and not to be judged. Postnatal depression is so common yet it's not

something you'd admit at a mothers' group unless you knew the other women well.

The comments from these women show how strongly they feel about the positive impact of talking to others. Talking enables all of us to learn more about anxiety and depression — through gaining understanding we are able to reduce the stigma. The more we talk about this, the more we normalise the occurrence of perinatal anxiety and depression.

IT IS NEVER TOO LATE TO START TALKING

My own children are starting to grow up now, and somehow their advancing age has given me the confidence to start talking. The first few years of their lives were consumed by my struggle with perinatal anxiety and depression. My husband and I were in such shock, panic and dismay that we talked to no-one for many years. We only survived as a family through the help of professionals, and a select number of family and friends.

I love being a mother now. I love my children passionately, I enjoy their company, I am proud of their achievements and I try to support them through their disappointments. They are by no means perfect children. I am no perfect mother. There are still days full of frustration with too much yelling and not enough acceptance. My husband and I have negotiated many untold clashes and have grown. My friends and I have reached a stage where we really can talk and share honestly. While we're all mothers we all do lots of other things too. We're all there for each other, and that's a very lucky place to be.

There is a very important reason why we should all start talking. Below are some very courageous words, moving in their simplicity. Simone has spent the last eight years encouraging mothers to start talking. That is her passion. She, along with her friends, began a foundation in memory of her sister. Gidget was a vibrant young mother who was surrounded by family and friends, yet felt so alone that she took her own life. Simone's message is very simple. We all need to start talking. If Gidget had felt she could start talking she would still be with us. While suicide is not common in women suffering from perinatal depression it still does happen. Every year in Australia some mothers feel so alone and distressed that they take their own lives.

Simone Short: this is why we need to start talking

We were all very unaware of Gidget's depression — the main symptom she displayed was extreme fatigue both during her pregnancy and in the months following. We had no idea what she was going through. There is no history of mental illness in our family.

The impact of her suicide was devastating and confusing — there were so many questions unanswered: how did this happen? why did it happen? what could I have done?

I took two weeks off work but was in shock for many months. We had a lot of family fly in from overseas and stay for a while, their presence was very comforting. We are a very close, open and happy family. It sounds like such a cliché but we never dreamt something like this would happen to us.

It is so disappointing that we did not know more at the time and we all miss her so much. She had a huge personality and our family dynamic has been changed forever. I often wonder how she would react to the things I go through as she was a very nurturing and kind big sister.

The foundation was started because her dearest friends felt they needed to do something to make a difference to mothers suffering from depression and anxiety. In the beginning it was very cathartic — getting together we would cry and laugh, but also learn about this illness we all knew nothing about.

The foundation has evolved into something much greater than just Gidget's story and we are all happy about that. We are comforted by the honesty of the many people who have shared their stories and have been inspired to get involved in what we do. I hope the name Gidget becomes a household name and 'allows' people to feel they can say 'I am doing it tough' or 'I need help'.

As you would imagine I was terrified of postnatal depression when I had my first child and everyone watched me very closely. I was very open with all my family and friends about how I was coping and admitted to the tough times almost in honour of Gidget — if that makes sense.

I had my second child and felt comfortable that I would be fine as I had got through those early years with my first. The second was a very easy textbook baby.

When I was pregnant with the twins I just kept telling myself I would be ok. I always dreamt of four children but did not know how I would cope. What a blessing they are. I have been challenged by them in ways I never imagined. Life can be such a juggle.

Since having the twins I have really starting wearing my motherhood crown loud and proud. Being so stretched emotionally and physically meant that just being a mum had to take priority over everything and everyone else in my life.

I have had arguments with bus drivers, people in Woolworths, even cafes over the chaotic presence of our big/little family, but at the end of the day what could be more important than raising four children?

The Gidget Foundation holds a biannual ladies' lunch. These lunches are always special, full of warmth and friendship as the spirit of motherhood is celebrated by hundreds of women. While we are always poignantly reminded of the reason for the lunch the speakers cleverly provide light-hearted anecdotes about the trials and tribulations of motherhood — something we can all relate to.

At every lunch women are reminded to start talking... the Gidget Foundation byline. And start talking we do, in the most deafening of ways. What is important, however, are the conversations shared among friends on these occasions. There are many, many stories of life-changing conversations: mothers and daughters sharing confidences, friends sharing intimate details of their true emotional state and their parenting challenges, new connections made between acquaintances. There is always lots of hugging, laughter and tears. It is very special to observe and experience the transformations that can occur when women are given the opportunity to start talking in such a caring environment. **www.gidgetfoundation.com.au**.

A NEW CULTURAL PARADIGM...

This is what we hope to achieve if we all start talking.

The world is full of sentimental and romantic baby quotes. Here are some well-known light-hearted reflections which can act as food for the soul and inspire you to start talking.

Everybody wants to save the earth; nobody wants to help Mom with the dishes. PJ O'Rourke
Motherhood has a very humanising effect. Everything gets reduced to essentials. Meryl Streep

When you have a baby, you set off an explosion in your marriage, and when the dust settles, your marriage is different from what it was. Not better, necessarily; not worse, necessarily; but different. Nora Ephron

Raising kids is part joy and part guerilla warfare. Ed Asner

A baby's a full time job for three adults. Nobody tells you that when you're pregnant... Nobody tells you how all-consuming it is to be a mother — how reading goes out the window and thinking too. Erica Jong

RESOURCES GUIDE

HELPLINES — NATIONAL

Perinatal anxiety and depression helplines

PANDA Post and Antenatal Depression Association Inc
1300 726 306
www.panda.org.au
PANDA is a Melbourne-based organisation which hosts a national counselling and information helpline.

PANDA offers peer counselling from trained volunteers who have usually experienced perinatal anxiety and depression themselves. PANDA can provide advice and referrals as well as counselling and support. Family members can receive counselling from PANDA, as well as the person who is experiencing perinatal anxiety and depression.

General depression helplines

beyondblue — the national depression initiative
1300 22 4636
www.beyondblue.org.au
As well as providing up-to-date and accurate information on depression, *beyondblue* has an information line which can help with information and referral advice both for those experiencing depression and their families.

Crisis helplines

Lifeline
13 11 14
www.lifeline.org.au
Trained volunteer telephone counsellors offer counselling and also information and support. Lifeline's website has a nationwide service finder tool and also self-help information and advice.

Suicide Call Back Service
1300 659 467
www.suicidecallbackservice.org.au
The Suicide Call Back Service provides crisis counselling to people at risk of suicide, their families and carers, and those bereaved by suicide. As well as providing crisis counselling, the service offers up to six further telephone counselling sessions.

Mental health — General

SANE Australia Helpline
1800 18 7263
www.sane.org
SANE offers information and referral on any aspect of mental health.

Support for men

Mensline Australia
1300 78 99 78
www.menslineaus.org.au
A national 24-hour telephone helpline service for men who are dealing with family and relationship difficulties.

Parenting helplines

Pregnancy, Birth and Baby Helpline
1800 882 436
www.healthdirect.org.au/pbb
Started in 2010, this is a Federal Government initiative which offers free telephone and website support for families and carers, from the first signs of pregnancy through to baby's first birthday. Information and referrals can

be provided on a huge number of topics, including conception, all aspects of pregnancy care, birthing, and the care of babies and their parents. The line is open 24 hours a day, seven days a week.

Parentline
Parentline offers counselling, information and referral on all aspects of parenting from trained professional counsellors.

Parentline Queensland and Northern Territory
1300 301 300
www.parentline.com.au

Parentline Victoria
13 22 89
www.parentline.vic.gov.au

Parent Helpline South Australia
1300 364 100
www.parenting.sa.gov.au

Parentline New South Wales
1300 130 052
www.parentline.org.au

Parent Help Centre Western Australia
08 9272 1466 or 1800 654 432
www.community.wa.gov.au/DFC/Resources/Helplines/
Parenting+WA+Line.htm

Parentline Australian Capital Territory
02 6287 3833
www.parentlineact.org.au

Parentline Tasmania
1300 808 178
www.dhhs.tas.gov.au/service_information/services_files/parentline

Breastfeeding helpline

Australian Breastfeeding Association
1800 686 2686
www.breastfeeding.asn.au
Trained volunteers offer support and advice on breastfeeding issues only.

Other helplines

Mensline Australia
1300 78 99 78
www.menslineaus.org.au
24-hour support for men with family and relationship problems, especially dealing with family breakdown or separation. This service provides anonymous telephone support, information and referral (cost of a local call).

Kids Helpline
1800 55 1800
Kids Helpline provides confidential telephone and online counselling for children and young people aged between five and 25 years.

INFORMATION AND SUPPORT

Perinatal anxiety and depression organisations/websites

PANDA Post and Antenatal Depression Association Inc
1300 726 306 (helpline)
03 9481 3377 (administration)
www.panda.org.au
810 Nicholson Street, North Fitzroy VIC 3068

PANDA is a Melbourne-based organisation which provides assistance and peer support to families all over Australia. PANDA commenced in the early 1980s when two women experiencing depression after their babies were born met to discuss the issues they faced. It grew into a self help group and from there expanded to provide a wide range of services. These include:
  •   a national helpline which offers peer counselling for those experiencing

perinatal anxiety and depression and their families and friends
- a Postnatal Depression Services Database
- a referral list of professionals who have expressed an interest in this area
- education about perinatal anxiety and depression for professionals and the wider community
- an excellent website with lots of fact sheets
- training and education programs for professionals and consumers including training in setting up support groups.

A DVD about anxiety and depression around childbirth has been produced and is available, a valuable resource for both professionals and those experiencing perinatal anxiety and depression.

Just Speak Up
www.justspeakup.com.au
Just Speak Up is a website set up by *beyondblue* (see below) which focuses solely on pre and postnatal anxiety and depression. There are many personal stories and you can add your own to the site, plus advice on where to find more information and support.

Write From The Heart
www.sheforpnd.com.au
Write From The Heart is a booklet available in hard copy and online as a PDF from a Western Australian group called She For PND. It is a terrific booklet, written from the heart as the title says and available free from the website.

Postpartum Support International
www.postpartum.net
This US-based website has a multitude of information and links to resources.

Overcoming PND
www.overcomingpnd.com
This is a UK-based website which has a host of information and some really practical advice eg on dealing with insomnia.

Trauma and Birth Stress
www.tabs.org.nz
Trauma and Birth Stress is a NZ-based organisation for women who have experienced PTSD after giving birth. The website has a lot of useful information.

280 BEYOND THE BABY BLUES

The Marce Society

www.marcesociety.com.au

The Australian branch of the International Marce Society is mainly focused on providing a forum where academics and professionals can share and exchange ideas and information. However, it is also aiming to bring the issues of mental health in the child rearing years into greater public awareness. The society organises regular conferences.

BLOGS

Postpartum Progress

www.postpartumprogress.com

This US-based blog by a mum called Katherine Stone has a wealth of information on all aspects of perinatal anxiety and depression.

Elaine Hanzak's Blog

www.elainehanzak.blogspot.com

www.hanzak.com

Elaine is a UK-based writer and speaker on perinatal depression and anxiety, and particularly on her own experience of puerperal psychosis.

General anxiety and depression organisations/ websites

beyondblue

1300 22 4636

www.beyondblue.org.au

beyondblue is Australia's national depression initiative, a not-for-profit organisation supported by the federal and state and territory governments. beyondblue deals in all forms of depression and anxiety, with a large portion of its website devoted to perinatal depression and anxiety.

beyondblue's website has excellent information and resources on perinatal anxiety and depression. beyondblue's Information Line can provide details of professionals who have registered with beyondblue, as well as general information and advice about coping with and treating anxiety and depression.

beyondblue's website has many downloadable resources in the form of fact sheets and booklets. Go to 'Get Information' and 'Download Information Materials'.

You can also ask for materials to be posted out to you, at no cost. There are several DVDs available, plus leaflets, booklets and books. To see a list on the *beyondblue* website go to: 'Get Information', 'Order Information Materials' and 'Individuals'.

Black Dog Institute
www.blackdoginstitute.org.au
The Black Dog Institute (BDI) is attached to the Prince of Wales Hospital in Randwick and is affiliated with the University of New South Wales; it is a research, clinical and educational facility specialising in mood disorders, including perinatal anxiety and depression. The BDI website has a large and useful section on perinatal anxiety and depression and a list of resources, mainly aimed at those living in NSW.

BDI has just created a six-hour accredited GP education program which includes a comprehensive participants' workbook.

BluePages
www.bluepages.anu.edu.au
BluePages is a comprehensive source of information that covers all types of depression. This is a straightforward and readable website with an emphasis on treatment and new research. It has a section called Blue Board which is an online support group for those experiencing depression and anxiety.

BluePages is managed by the Depression and Anxiety Consumer Research Unit and the Centre for Mental Health Research at the Australian National University in Canberra.

Reconnexion
www.reconnexion.org.au
This not-for-profit organisation provides counselling and support for people with anxiety and panic disorders, depression and also tranquiliser dependency.

The Anxiety Panic Hub
www.panicattacks.com.au
Information and book sales website by author Bronwyn Fox.

DepNet
www.depnet.com.au
Depnet is a depression information service which uses an interactive website to disseminate knowledge about depression and to support those who are experiencing depression and their families. You can write a private diary and connect with others through the forum and community.

Lifeline Service Finder
www.justlook.org.au
The Lifeline Service Finder is a searchable directory of services and assistance available all over Australia. Topics covered include mental health services, family and children's services and financial assistance.

The website lists free or low cost health and community services available in Australia. It includes accommodation, domestic violence, family and children's services, financial assistance and mental health services.

Living Is For Everyone
www.livingisforeveryone.com.au
The Commonwealth Government's Living Is For Everyone (LIFE) website is a resource centre for suicide and self-harm prevention. It is designed to aid communication between stakeholders across Australia and does not provide crisis counselling or intervention. On the website you will find information about the best evidence and resources available for those in the field of suicide and self-harm prevention.

Multicultural mental health

Multicultural Mental Health Australia
02 9840 3333
www.mmha.org.au
Multicultural Mental Health Australia (MMHA) is a national program funded by the Australian Government to improve mental health awareness and suicide prevention in culturally and linguistically diverse (CALD) communities through a variety of projects. This includes developing resources and information about key mental health issues in a variety of community languages.

Medication use in pregnancy and when breastfeeding

beyondblue
www.beyondblue.org.au
beyondblue publishes an information sheet: *Notes on antidepressant medication in pregnancy and lactation.*

MotherSafe NSW Medications in Pregnancy and Breastfeeding Service
02 9382 6539 (Sydney metropolitan area)
1800 647 848 (Non-metropolitan area)

www.mothersafe.org.au
Mothersafe is a free service for women and healthcare providers in NSW, providing information about the use of drugs in pregnancy and when breastfeeding. Other exposures such as street drugs, infections and occupational exposures can also be discussed. MotherSafe also publishes several factsheets.

In other states, women and healthcare staff can call the *National Prescribing Service* NPS Medicines Line 1300 888 763

OTIS — Organization of Teratology Information Specialists
www.otispregnancy.org
This USA-based organisation provides accurate evidence-based, clinical information to patients and health care professionals about exposures during pregnancy and lactation. The website has many factsheets as well as news and other resources.

Motherisk
www.motherisk.org
This Canadian website also has a huge amount of information on the use of medications in pregnancy and while breastfeeding.

INTERNET-BASED MENTAL HEALTH PROGRAMS

Self-help programs delivered via the internet are becoming increasingly popular and accessible. Two of the better known ones available in Australia are described below.

beyondblue has a directory of e-mental health services and therapies which clearly explains the key points, advantages and disadvantages of each. See www.beyondblue.org.au, click on the 'Get Help' tab.

MoodGYM
www.moodgym.anu.edu.au
MoodGYM is a cognitive behaviour therapy training program that is delivered online. Cognitive behavioural therapy is a proven treatment for depression (see Chapters 6 and 7 for more information).

MoodGYM has been developed and is maintained by staff at the Centre for Mental Health Research at the Australian National University in Canberra. It was originally aimed at preventing depression in young people but has since been studied as a treatment for depression in itself.

The MoodGYM website stresses: *'The information provided throughout MoodGYM is intended for **information and skill development purposes only**. MoodGYM is not a substitute for seeking diagnosis and treatment from a qualified person.'*

CRUfAD
www.crufad.org
CRUfAD is a research unit, part of St Vincent's Hospital in Sydney, which is exploring online education and treatment of disorders including anxiety and depression. There is a lot of information to read on the website, and information about their online treatment options.

MEDICARE ASSISTANCE

Your GP can talk you through all the local mental health services in your area.

On the PANDA website there is a very useful overview of public mental health services throughout Australia: www.panda.org.au. Follow links to 'Practical Information', 'Support Services' and 'Mental Health'.

Funding/government support

Medicare benefits for pregnancy support counselling
Medicare rebates are available for pregnancy-related counselling by a GP, psychologist, social worker or mental health nurse. Each woman can receive three rebates for each pregnancy and these can be used either whilst pregnant or in the 12 months following the pregnancy.

The counselling provided must be 'non-directive' which is described in the Department of Health and Ageing's factsheet as:
The service involves the counsellor undertaking a safe, confidential process that helps the patient explore concerns they have about a pregnancy. This includes providing unbiased, evidence-based information about all options and services available to the patient, where requested.

Exclusions: GPs, psychologists, social workers and mental health nurses who have a direct pecuniary interest in a health service that has as its primary purpose the provision of pregnancy termination services cannot provide non-directive pregnancy support counselling services under Medicare.

In most cases when a private practitioner provides the counselling there will be a gap payment to be made, however, some professionals may provide bulk billing for counselling.

For more information, see: www.psychology.org.au/medicare/

Medicare GP Mental Health Care Rebates — Better Access to Mental Health Care

If you have been diagnosed with perinatal anxiety and/or depression, your GP can prepare a mental health care plan for you and can refer you for up to 12 counselling sessions with a suitable professional: usually a clinical psychologist, sometimes a specialist GP or allied health professional.

Patients may receive up to 12 individual services (plus six more under exceptional circumstances) and up to 12 group therapy sessions.

The rebate amount varies depending on the length of the counselling session and on which professional provides it. There will usually be a gap payment to be made by the patient.

You can read more about this at: www.psychology.org.au/medicare/

beyondblue has a fact sheet about Better Access to Mental Health Care: see 'Get Information' and 'Download Information Materials' section of the website. It is Factsheet 24.

ATAPS — Access To Allied Psychological Services

12 counselling sessions per year

If you have been diagnosed with a perinatal anxiety or depression then your GP may have access to ATAPS funded resources/treatments at no cost to you.

Only patients who are not using the GP Mental Health Care Rebates described above can access ATAPS services.

Your GP can refer you for up to 12 counselling sessions per year with either: a psychologist, social worker, mental health nurse, occupational therapist, or Aboriginal and Torres Straits Islander heath worker (known as allied health professionals). These can be individual or group therapy sessions. Your GP needs to have in place a GP Mental Health Treatment Plan for you, and must do a review with you after the first six sessions.

For more information, see:

www.health.gov.au/internet/main/publishing.nsf/Content/mental-boimhc-ataps

PROFESSIONAL SUPPORT

When you are looking for treatment for perinatal anxiety and depression, it is recommended that you seek professionals who have a great deal of experience in the area. Your GP can support you as you find the people to assist, but there are other places to find useful referrals.

PANDA — Post and Antenatal Depression Association Inc
1300 726 306
www.panda.org.au
PANDA has a list of medical and allied health professionals who have an interest in this area and who have registered with PANDA.

beyondblue
1300 22 4636
www.beyondblue.org.au
beyondblue has a Directory of Medical and Allied Health Practitioners in Mental Health. Medical or mental health professionals who have chosen to register in *beyondblue* can be found here, including many with expertise in perinatal anxiety and depression.

Psychologists
1800 333 497
www.psychology.org.au
The Australian Psychological Society (APS) is the largest professional association for psychologists with over 15,000 members. On the website, you can click on *Find A Psychologist* or you can call and ask for the Australian Psychological Society Referral Line. For information on Medicare rebates for psychological therapy see page 285.

Australian Psychological Society Referral Line
1800 333 497
The APS offers a *'Find a Psychologist'* service from this line.

Psychiatrists
Your GP is usually the first port of call when searching for a psychiatrist as you need a GP referral to visit one. PANDA, see above, has a list of psychiatrists with experience in the field of perinatal anxiety and depression. *beyondblue* also has a directory of professionals listing psychiatrists.

SUPPORT GROUPS

If there is a postnatal depression support group in your area, then you need to know about it. Some support groups will also offer help to friends and family.

PANDA Helpline
1300 726 306
The PANDA Helpline can supply information about support groups in your area. You can speak to one of the peer counsellors who can access their national database of information and resources to check what might be available in your part of the country.

PANDA can also assist people who hope to set up a support group, and have written a Guide to Postnatal Depression Support Groups. This is available from the PANDA website.

The PANDA website has a terrific section on Community Support: www. panda.org.au/practical-information/support-services/community-support

beyondblue
www.beyondblue.org.au
beyondblue has a information and resource lists for each state on their website. You can easily download these and check to see whether they include any information about support groups local to you.

The Black Dog Institute
www.blackdoginstitute.org.au
In the Resources section there is a list of support groups.

FOR DADS

Support and advice for men

Men experiencing symptoms of anxiety and depression can receive assistance first and foremost from PANDA (see above). Similarly if your partner has anxiety or depression, PANDA can support you as her carer.

beyondblue (see above) and the Black Dog Institute (see above) websites have sections aimed specifically at blokes.

The following are additional resources which may be of help for some men.

Hey Dad
1300 22 4636 *beyondblue*
beyondblue.com.au, follow links to 'Get Information' and 'Download Information Materials'. *beyondblue* teamed up with Hey Dad WA at Ngala (see page 313) to publish a booklet called *Hey Dad, Fatherhood — First 12 months*. It can be ordered or downloaded from the *beyondblue* website. This is a really terrific resource, covering pregnancy, early parenthood, and anxiety and depression, all from a dad's perspective.

Mensline Australia
1300 78 99 78
www.menslineaus.org.au
Mensline is a 24-hour, seven day telephone support, information and referral service. Men are welcome to call when experiencing perinatal anxiety or depression or when their partners are. The website also has an online support forum and a service database.

Postpartum Men
www.postpartummen.com
This is a US-based website, set up by a psychotherapist who works with men experiencing perinatal anxiety and depression. It has many resources and an online self-assessment tool.

Postpartum Dads
www.postpartumdads.org
A similar website to the one above, there are many personal stories on this website. It is a good place to find support and information.

Men and Depression
www.nimh.nih.gov
The US-based National Institute for Mental Health has a great deal of information, including videos about depression. Follow links to 'Mental Health Information', 'By Age/Gender' and 'Men'.

The Shed Online
www.theshedonline.org.au
The Shed Online is an internet-based social community for men, founded by *beyondblue: the national depression initiative*, The Movember Foundation and the Australian Men's Shed Association.

PARENTING WEBSITES — GENERAL

Raising Children Network
www.raisingchildren.net.au
This is the main government-funded Australian parenting website with heaps of information about caring for children. The website has factsheets, videos and a busy parent forum.

Pregnancy, Birth and Baby Helpline
1800 882 436
www.healthdirect.org.au/pbb
(see page 276)

My Child
www.mychild.gov.au
My Child is the Australian Federal Government's website on childcare. Here you can find information on different types of childcare and on financial assistance.

Home Buddies
www.homebuddies.com.au
This is an online listing service with a focus on services and products for the home and family.

Parent Wellbeing
www.parentwellbeing.com
This website and blog, by Jodie Benveniste, helps families to take care of themselves whilst raising young children.

The Bub Hub
www.bubhub.com.au
This website centres on pregnancy, babies and parenting. It has a busy forum and services directory as well as articles and competitions/giveaways.

Essential Baby
www.essentialbaby.com.au
Essential Baby is a Fairfax digital website with a focus on pregnancy, babies, children and parenting. It has lots of news and articles, plus friendly forums and blogs.

Australian Multiple Birth Association (AMBA)
www.amba.org
Information about parenting twins, pregnancy and birth and an active online forum for support.

Self Care
www.raisingchildren.net.au/looking_after_yourself/looking_after_yourself.html

Relationship support

Relationships Australia
1300 364 277
www.relationships.com.au
Relationships Australia provides face to face counselling and support and an online service. The website is full of relationship information and resources.

STATE RESOURCES

ACT

The **PANDA Helpline** can provide up to date listings of support groups, therapy groups and resources in the ACT: 1300 726 306.

PANDSI (see below) can offer information and referrals specific to the ACT.

Perinatal mental health — support and resources

PANDSI (Post and Antenatal Depression Support and Information)
02 6232 6664 (Support and Information)
02 6232 6277 (Administration)
www.pandsi.org
25 Stapylton Street, Holder ACT 2611

PANDSI has been in operation for more than 30 years and provides support and information to families affected by post or antenatal depression. Services include telephone support, combined exercise and support groups, facilitated support groups with free childcare, pram walking group, video and book lending library, quarterly newsletter and information packs.

PANDSI has an informative website which details all the services offered:
- support group
- partner and family information sessions
- men's information sessions
- pram walking group.

You can become a member of PANDSI and receive its quarterly newsletter.

Perinatal Mental Health Consultation Service
02 6205 1469
www.health.act.gov.au (search for perinatal mental health)
Callam Offices

Easy Street, Woden ACT 2606
This ACT Health service comprises a multi-disciplinary team (psychiatrist, psychologist, nurse and others) who hold a bi-weekly clinic. A referral from a health professional is needed, there is clear information on the website about the referral process.

Parenting support and resources

Parentline ACT
02 6287 3833
www.parentlineact.org.au
Parentline offers telephone counselling, support and referral from the helpline and there is lots of useful information on the website. Face-to-face counselling and regular volunteer telephone counselling is also available. Paint and Play is a weekly playgroup run by Parentline.

Tresillian Parent Helpline
1800 637 357
(See page 295)

QEII Family Centre
02 6205 2333
www.cmsinc.org.au
129 Carruthers St, Curtin ACT 2605
The Queen Elizabeth II Family Centre is a residential stay centre where families with children up to the age of three years can be assisted with parenting issues.

Family and carer support

Carers ACT
02 6296 9900
1800 242 636 (toll free)
www.carersact.asn.au
Churches Centre
54 Benjamin Way, Belconnen ACT 2617
Carers ACT provides counselling, advice, advocacy, education and training to carers. The National Carer Counselling Program is managed by Carers ACT. Carers can receive six free counselling sessions from a professionally trained and qualified counsellor either in person or by telephone. More general telephone support and counselling is available at any time on the telephone number above.

NSW

The **PANDA Helpline** can provide up to date listings of support groups, therapy groups and resources in NSW: 1300 726 306.

The **Black Dog Institute** has a list of NSW resources on its website (see page 281).

The **Gidget Foundation** website also has resources on its website (see below).

Perinatal mental health — support and resources

Gidget Foundation
www.gidgetfoundation.com.au
The Gidget Foundation promotes awareness of perinatal anxiety and depression amongst women, families, health providers and the community. The Gidget website has personal stories, information sheets and information about awareness campaigns. The Gidget Foundation has links with many carer and medical groups in Sydney and runs workshops and research projects. It was a partner with PANDA in producing a DVD released in 2010.

Tresillian — Perinatal anxiety and depression therapy programs
(see Tresillian below)
The Tresillian Family Care Centres at Canterbury and Wollstonecraft hold regular perinatal anxiety and depression therapy group programs. Women are referred to the groups from a health professional, such as their local doctor or child and family health nurse. Pre-group interviews are conducted with each woman by the group facilitator.

Karitane — Jade House
(see Karitane below)
Services offered include: individual and couple therapy, psychiatric help, day stay, parenting and child development information, mother-infant therapy groups, anxiety-management groups, postnatal issues groups. Jade House is for women and their families living within the Sydney South West Area Health Service (SSWAHS).

Beat Baby Blues

www.beatbabyblues.com.au

The St John of God Hospitals (SJOGH) in Burwood and Richmond have been helping mums and mums-to-be since 1984. SJOGH is the largest not-for-profit provider of mental health care in NSW and runs a mother and baby unit at its Burwood Hospital and day care support at its Richmond Hospital. The Beat Baby Blues website provides general information on perinatal depression and its treatment as well as information about the in and outpatient services offered by SJOGH.

NSW Mental Health Association

02 9339 6000

1300 794 991 (Information service)

1300 794 992 (Anxiety Disorders Information)

www.mentalhealth.asn.au

Level 5, 80 William Street, East Sydney NSW 2011

The NSW Mental Health Association provides an anonymous and free telephone and email Information Hotline during business hours. Qualified staff are able to assist by tapping into a specialised database which can help you find solutions to your problems. There are also groups and self-help programs available.

Parenting support and resources

Karitane

9794 2300

1300 227 464 (24-hour careline)

www.karitane.com.au

Cnr The Horsley Drive & Mitchell Street, Carramar NSW 2163

Karitane has been providing parenting services to families of children up to five years since 1923 and has centres in Sydney's western and eastern suburbs. There are Family Care Centres in Liverpool and Randwick, and a Residential Family Care Unit at Carramar. Jade House in Fairfield Heights is a specialised day stay and counselling unit for women who have a diagnosis of a perinatal anxiety or depression or are at risk.

Karitane is a very large organisation with many programs and groups. These include: advice for new parents, group and individual counselling, a psychologist available for CBT, day stays for feeding, settling, and parenting issues, a postnatal depression group, residential stays and a toddler behaviour clinic.

The Karitane Careline is open 24 hours every day and is staffed by experienced child health nurses who can answer questions on child health and wellbeing and offer advice on many aspects of parenting.

Tresillian
02 9787 0800
02 9787 0855 (24-hour Tresillian Parent Helpline — Sydney)
1800 637 357 (24-hour Tresillian Parent Helpline — Freecall outside Sydney)
www.tresillian.net
Tresillian Canterbury Head Office
McKenzie Street, Belmore NSW 2192
Tresillian Family Care Centres are located in Canterbury, Nepean, Willoughby and Wollstonecraft and provide a wide variety of services for the families. The Tresillian 24-Hour Parent Helpline provides advice and referral to families throughout NSW and there is a live online support service available through Facebook. Tresillian provides support to families with children aged up to the age of five years only.

Services offered from the centres include: outreach, parenting programs, day stay, residential stays, and occasional and long daycare in the Wollstonecraft centre.

Good Beginnings
02 9211 6767
www.goodbeginnings.net.au
Suite 38, 8–24 Kippax Street, Surry Hills NSW 2010
Good Beginnings offers volunteer home visiting and other programs designed to assist families with young children. Call their offices to ask for more information on what is currently available.

Aboriginal services

Some area health services have specific support for Aboriginal families, eg the **South East Sydney Area Health Service**, call 02 9319 5823. Contact your local area health service to ask.

The Royal Hospital for Women in Sydney has an Aboriginal child and family health nurse, call 02 9382 6783.

Multicultural services

NSW Multicultural Health Communication Service
02 9816 0346

www.mhcs.health.nsw.gov.au
Old Gladesville Hospital
Punt Road, Gladesville NSW 2111
The MHCS provides translations of a range of health information, including leaflets on mental health in pregnancy and after birth.

NSW Transcultural Mental Health Centre
02 9840 3800
www.dhi.gov.au (follow link to 'Transcultural Mental Health Centre')
Cumberland Hospital
5 Fleet Street, North Parramatta NSW 2151
THE TMHC provides clinical services, health promotion, publications and education and training. It is a statewide service, promoting wider access to mental health services for people of cultural and linguistic diversity background.

Family and carer support

Carers NSW
02 9280 4744
1800 242 636 (toll free)
www.carersnsw.asn.au
Roden Cutler House
Level 18, 24 Campbell St, Sydney NSW 2000
Carers NSW provides counselling, advice, advocacy, education and training for carers. The National Carer Counselling Program is managed by Carers NSW. Carers can receive six free counselling sessions from a professionally trained and qualified counsellor either in person or by telephone. More general telephone support and counselling is available at any time on the telephone number above.

Other state-based helplines and support services

NALAG (Association for Loss and Grief) NSW
02 9988 3376
www.nalag.org.au
NALAG (NSW) Inc provides education and support for those suffering loss, grief and bereavement across NSW. NALAG has centres and branches all over NSW. The helpful website has lots of information and resources.

NT

The **PANDA Helpline** can provide up to date listings of support groups, therapy groups and resources in the Northern Territory: 1300 726 306.

Parenting support and resources

Parentline
1300 301 300
www.parentline.com.au
Trained counsellors can answer questions on all aspects of parenting children, they also provide information, referral and telephone parenting programs. Web counselling is also provided.

Good Beginnings
0488 220 135 (National Programs Coordinator)
www.goodbeginnings.org.au
Good Beginnings offers programs designed to assist families with young children. Call their offices to ask for more information.

Family and carer support

Carers NT
08 8944 4888
1800 242 636 (toll free)
www.nt.carersaustralia.com.au
59 Bayview Boulevard, Bayview NT 0820
Carers NT provides counselling, advice, advocacy, education and training to carers. The National Carer Counselling Program is managed by Carers NT. Carers can receive six free counselling sessions from a professionally trained and qualified counsellor either in person or by telephone. More general telephone support and counselling is available at any time on the telephone number above.

Mental Health Carers NT
08 89481051
www.arafmi.org
PO Box 40556, Casuarina NT 0811
Mental Health Carers NT provides support, advocacy and education for carers of those with a mental illness of any sort.

QLD

The **PANDA Helpline** can provide up to date listings of support groups, therapy groups and resources in Queensland: 1300 726 306.

Perinatal mental health — support and resources

Women's Health Queensland Wide Inc
07 3839 9962
07 3839 9988 (Queensland-wide Health Information Line)
1800 017 676 (Queensland-wide Health Information Line — toll free)
www.womhealth.org.au
165 Gregory Terrace, Spring Hill QLD 4000
Women's Health Queensland Wide is a not-for-profit organisation which provides education, information and support to women and health workers. The organisation has a free lending library (books can be posted out) with a good selection of books on antenatal and postnatal anxiety and depression. The website has information, in the form of a very readable booklet called *Antenatal and Postnatal Depression*, which can be posted out or downloaded as a PDF. You can call the Information Line to ask about any aspect of health and wellbeing for women.

The Brisbane Centre for Post Natal Disorders
07 3398 0111
www.belmontprivate.com.au (follow links to 'Programs and Services' and 'Post Natal Disorders')
Belmont Private Hospital
1220 Creek Road, Carina QLD 4152
The Brisbane Centre for Post Natal Disorders provides treatment and support for women experiencing perinatal mood disorders. There is a mother and baby unit, plus day patients' programs and individual counselling. Fathers' groups are held and telephone support services continue after discharge.

Parenting support and resources

Parentline
1300 301 300
www.parentline.com.au

Trained counsellors can answer questions on all aspects of parenting children, they also provide information, referral and telephone parenting programs. Web counselling is also provided.

Child Health Line
1800 177 279
Child Health Line is run by the Queensland Government's Community Child Health Service. Child health nurses man the line and can answer your questions and refer you for further help or advice.

Ellen Barron Early Parenting Centre
07 3139 6500
www.health.qld.gov.au (search for 'Ellen Barron')
Hamilton Road, Chermside QLD 4032
The Ellen Barron Early Parenting Centre offers a residential program for families with children from birth to three years who are experiencing complex parenting issues including anxiety and depression. Referrals are made by GPs, paediatricians or other health professionals.

Good Beginnings
0419 201 405 (State Coordinator)
www.goodbeginnings.org.au
Good Beginnings offers programs designed to assist families with young children. Call their offices to ask for more information on what is currently available.

Multicultural services

Queensland Transcultural Mental Health Centre
07 3167 8333
www.health.qld.gov.au/pahospital/qtmhc
519 Kessels Road, MacGregor QLD 4109
Queensland TMHC is a specialist mental health service for people of non-English speaking background. It offers a Transcultural Clinical Consultation Service (TCCS) which acts as an adjunct to mainstream mental health services to ensure that services provided are culturally and linguistically appropriate.

Family and carer support

Arafmi — Mental Health Carers
07 3254 1881

1800 35 1881 (toll free from outside Brisbane)
www.arafmiqld.org
Arafmi offers 24-hour telephone support to carers of people with mental health issues, groups are also run in many locations. Arafmi's focus is specifically on supporting carers, respite and support programs are available and several different types of workshops are run regularly.

Carers Queensland
07 3900 8100
1800 242 636 (toll free)
www.qld.carersaustralia.com.au
15 Abbott St, Camp Hill QLD 4121
Carers QLD provides counselling, advice, advocacy, education and training to carers. The National Carer Counselling Program is managed by Carers QLD. Carers can receive six free counselling sessions from a professionally trained and qualified counsellor either in person or by telephone. More general telephone support and counselling is available at any time on the telephone number above.

SA

The **PANDA Helpline** can provide up to date listings of support groups, therapy groups and resources in South Australia: 1300 726 306.

Perinatal mental health — support and resources

Helen Mayo House
08 8303 1183
www.wch.sa.gov.au/services/az/divisions/mentalhealth/helenmayo/index.html
226 Fullarton Road, Glenside SA 5065
Helen Mayo House is an acute mother and baby service providing inpatient and outpatient services. It also provides information and referrals on all aspects of perinatal anxiety and depression to both patients and clinicians throughout South Australia. Helen Mayo House is part of the Women and Children's Hospital in Adelaide.

The staff of Helen Mayo House are available by telephone 24 hours a day, seven days a week to counsel and advise parents who are experiencing difficulties when pregnant or having had a baby.

General Practice Perinatal Shared Care Workers
08 8303 1451 (business hours)
Two specialist perinatal mental health workers work with local GPs and other members of the community to assist parents experiencing anxiety and depression before and after childbirth. The workers have lists of local resources in both the city and country which may be useful, especially to those who live in rural and remote areas.

Aceda
08 8297 7108 (business hours)
www.aceda.org.au
589 South Road, Everard Park SA 5035
Aceda is an organisation supporting people experiencing anxiety and panic disorders, as well as obsessive compulsive and eating disorders. It is a not-for-profit organisation which offers free telephone peer support, plus workshops, groups and other programs. Aceda has a terrific website with a lot of very user-friendly information.

Parenting support and resources

Parenting South Australia
1300 364 100 (Parent Helpline)
www.parenting.sa.gov.au
Parenting SA was founded by the state government in 1996 and aims to support parents and families in all aspects of parenting. A helpline is available 24 hours a day, seven days a week offering advice, support and referral on all child-related matters.
Parenting SA has produced many Parent Easy Guides, which are fact sheets available free to parents and families. The Parenting SA website has a useful tool which can help you find a parenting or parent education group in your area.

Torrens House
www.cyh.com (follow links to 'Parenting and child health', 'Services' and 'Torrens House')
295 South Terrace, Adelaide SA 5000
A facility of the Children, Youth and Women's Health Service, Torrens House provides a free, live-in service to families with young children who require assistance with unresolved feeding, settling and sleeping issues. Families stay from Tuesday–Friday and receive intensive support from staff including nursing staff, medical officers, a mental health nurse and a social worker.

Good Beginnings
0438 800 914 (National Programs Coordinator)
www.goodbeginnings.org.au
Good Beginnings offers programs designed to assist families with young children. Call their offices to ask for more information on what is currently available.

Family and carer support

Carers SA — Supporting Family Carers
08 8291 5600
1800 242 636 (toll free)
www.sa.carersaustralia.com.au
58 King William Rd, Goodwood SA 5034
Carers SA provides counselling, advice, advocacy, education and training to carers. The National Carer Counselling Program is managed by Carers SA, carers can receive six free counselling sessions from a professionally trained

and qualified counsellor either in person or by telephone. More general telephone support and counselling is available at any time on the telephone number above.

TAS

The **PANDA Helpline** can provide up to date listings of support groups, therapy groups and resources in Tasmania: 1300 726 306.

Perinatal mental health — support and resources

Parenting Centres
03 6326 6188 (North)
03 6434 6201 (North West)
03 6233 2700 (South)
www.dhhs.tas.gov.au (search for 'Parenting Centres')
Parenting Centres are a service of the Department of Health and Human Services and offer assistance to families and carers who need extra support and who have children aged up to five years. They are a day service and are manned by social workers, psychologists, and child and family health nurses.

Parenting Centres can assist with all sorts of problems and one area of focus is anxiety and depression in parents. Support may be offered on an individual or group basis and home visits may be available.

St Helen's Private Mother and Baby Unit
03 6221 6444
www.healthscopehospitals.com.au (click on Tasmania)
186 Macquarie Street, Hobart TAS 7000
St Helen's Private Mother and Baby Unit provides in-patient care to mothers and babies with issues of baby care (eg sleeping, feeding issues) and/or antenatal or postnatal anxiety or depression. The unit is staffed by midwives and nurses specialising both in maternal and child health and in psychiatry. There are some places for public patients.

Parenting support and resources

Child Health Centres
www.dhhs.tas.gov.au (search for 'child health centres')
Call the Parenting Line 1300 808 178 to ask where your nearest centre is.
Child Health Centres offer support to families with children under the age of five. Child and family health nurses carry out the checks in your baby's 'blue book' and can offer a great deal of support and advice to parents.

Early Support for Parents
03 6223 2937
www.earlysupport4parents.com
Early Support For Parents is a volunteer home-visiting program based in southern Tasmania. Trained volunteers support families in their own homes with the aim of easing the stresses of parenthood.

The Parenting Line
1300 808 178 (cost of a local call)
24 hours, 7 days a week
The Parenting Line is an information and advice service for parents and carers, staffed by trained professionals. It can be used for advice and support at any time and in acute times of stress.

Parenting Centres
03 6326 6188 (North)
03 6434 6201 (North West)
03 6233 2700 (South)
www.dhhs.tas.gov.au (search for 'Parenting Centres')
See above

Good Beginnings Tasmania
03 6223 5810 or 0439 025 124
www.goodbeginnings.org.au
6 Washington Street, South Hobart TAS 7004
Brighton Community & Health Centre
27 Greenpoint Road, Bridgewater TAS 7030
Good Beginnings Tasmania offers volunteer home visiting and other programs designed to assist families with young children. Call their offices to ask for more information on what is currently available. Postnatal support groups are run at times.

Support for dads

Good Beginnings (see above) publishes a variety of informative leaflets for dads including one on postnatal depression.

Family and carer support

Carers Tasmania
03 6231 5507

www.tas.carersaustralia.com.au
64 Burnett Street, North Hobart TAS 7000
Carers TAS provides counselling, advice, advocacy, education and training to carers. The National Carer Counselling Program is managed by Carers TAS. Carers can receive six free counselling sessions from a professionally trained and qualified counsellor either in person or by telephone. More general telephone support and counselling is available at any time on the telephone number above.

Association of Relatives and Friends of the Mentally Ill (ARAFMI)
03 62287448
Hobart Office
3 Bowen Road, Moonah TAS 7009
03 6331 4486
Launceston Office
34 Howick Street, Launceston TAS 7250
www.arafmitas.org.au
ARAFMI runs groups for families and carers of those with a mental illness, as well as offering support and advice. There are also some groups for people experiencing depression.

VIC

The **PANDA Helpline** can provide up to date listings of support groups, therapy groups and resources in Victoria: 1300 726 306.

Perinatal mental health — support and resources

PANDA — Post and Antenatal Depression Association Inc
1300 726 306 (Helpline)
03 9481 3377 (Administration)
www.panda.org.au
810 Nicholson Street, North Fitzroy VIC 3068
PANDA is a Melbourne-based organisation which provides assistance and peer support to families all over Australia. PANDA commenced in the early 1980s when two women experiencing depression after their babies were born met to discuss the issues they faced. It grew into a self help group and from there expanded to provide a wide range of services. These include:
- a national helpline which offers peer counselling for those experiencing perinatal depression and their families and friends
- a Postnatal Depression Services Database
- a referral list of professionals who have expressed an interest in this area
- education about perinatal depression for professionals and the wider community
- an excellent website with lots of fact sheets
- training and education programs for professionals and consumers including training in setting up support groups.

A DVD about anxiety and depression around childbirth has been produced and is available, a valuable resource for both professionals and those experiencing perinatal depression.

The Raphael Centres, Berwick, Geelong and Warrnambool
03 9707 3988
Raphael Centre Berwick
57 Fairholme Boulevard, Berwick VIC 3806
03 5221 7333
St John of God Raphael Centre Geelong
11 Fenwick Street, Geelong VIC 3220
03 5564 0636

Raphael Centre, South West Victoria
St John of God Hospital Warrnambool
136 Botanic Road, Warrnambool VIC 3280
www.sjog.org.au (follow link to 'Other Services')
The three Raphael Centres provide support, advice and treatment for families experiencing anxiety and depression around childbirth and the early years of parenthood. The centres offer telephone support, group programs and workshops for anxiety and depression, and parenting programs. You do not have to have private health insurance to attend a Raphael Centre.

Parent-Infant Research Institute (PIRI)
03 9496 4496 (The Infant Clinic)
Heidelberg Repatriation Hospital
Level 1, Centaur Building
300 Waterdale Road, Heidelberg Heights VIC 3081
www.piri.org.au
PIRI is a research and clinical institute which develops and applies evidence-based treatments to improve the emotional wellbeing of parents and infants. PIRI runs the Infant Clinic, where parents can find help for issues in the first year of a child's life. PIRI also runs many classes, courses and workshops and publishes parenting literature. There is a group therapy program for those experiencing postnatal depression, and many other programs which would be of value to those who are at risk of or experiencing anxiety and depression related to childbirth.

Anxiety Disorders Association of Victoria
03 9853 8089
www.adavic.org.au
ADAVIC provides support, information and resources to those affected by anxiety, depression and related issues as well as their family and carers. Phone and email support is available, as are support groups and workshops. The website has lots of information plus a forum and a 'Find a Therapist' function.

Perinatal Psychology
03 9486 8777
www.perinatalpsychology.com.au
This private psychology clinic specialises in treating families experiencing anxiety and depression in the perinatal period. Groups are run and individual consultations provided. Workshops and other training programs for professionals are offered.

Parenting support and resources

Good Beginnings
0438 800 914
www.goodbeginnings.org.au
Good Beginnings offers programs designed to assist families with young children. Call their offices to ask for more information on what programs are currently available.

Multicultural services

Victorian Transcultural Psychiatry Unit
www.vtpu.org.au
St Vincent's Hospital
Level 2, Bolte Wing
Nicholson Street, Fitzroy VIC 3065
The aim of the VTPU is to improve the quality and accessibility of mental health services to people from culturally and linguistically diverse backgrounds. See the extensive website for full details.

Family and carer support

Carers Victoria
03 9396 9500
1800 242 636 (toll free)
www.carersvictoria.org.au
Level 1, 37 Albert Street, Footscray VIC 3011
Carers Vic provides counselling, advice, advocacy, education and training to carers. The National Carer Counselling Program is managed by Carers Vic. Carers can receive six free counselling sessions from a professionally trained and qualified counsellor either in person or by telephone. More general telephone support and counselling is available at any time on the telephone number above.

ARAFEMI Victoria
03 9810 9300
www.arafemi.org.au
Amongst its many other services, ARAFEMI provides support to the families and carers of those experiencing a mental illness.

Other state helplines

Suicide Helpline — Victoria
1300 651 251
www.suicidehelpline.org.au
24-hour counselling, crisis intervention, information and referral.

NALAG — National Association for Loss and Grief (VIC)
03 329 4003
1800 100 023
www.nalagvic.org.au
This is not a helpline as such but there are many resources listed on the website.

WA

The **PANDA Helpline** can provide up to date listings of support groups, therapy groups and resources in Western Australia: 1300 726 306.

For further up-to-date information on resources and support services in WA, see the **From the Heart** website below.

Perinatal mental health — support and resources

From the Heart WA — *Supporting Perinatal Mental Health*
Formerly Post Natal Depression Support Association (PNDSA) Inc
08 9340 1688 (Administration)
08 9340 1622 (Support)
info@fromtheheartwa.org.au
www.fromtheheartwa.org.au
PO Box 548, Subiaco WA 6904
From the Heart WA is a consumer group which has been in operation since 1997. Founded by a small group of mothers who had experienced postnatal depression, it has grown to be a powerful voice for families and provides several valuable services. It offers information and support for families all over WA. Regular support groups are run in Perth, and From the Heart WA provides advice and training to others wishing to set up support groups.

The From the Heart WA website has a comprehensive guide to all the services and support available in WA. Also available is the excellent resource Write From The Heart a booklet outlining perinatal anxiety and disorder, containing many personal stories. This can be downloaded as a PDF from the website, or a copy can be posted if requested. It has sound practical advice, warm, personal stories and a good contact list.

The Raphael Centre — Subiaco
08 9382 6828
1300 306 828 (cost of a local call)
www.sjog.org.au (follow link to 'Other Services')
St John of God House
177–179 Cambridge Street, Subiaco WA 6008
The Raphael Centre provides information and support for families affected by perinatal anxiety and depression from pregnancy until the children are

three years of age. Services include:

- telephone support and information — numbers above
- Therapeutic Group — a treatment and support group, with additional support available for partners
- Antenatal and Postnatal Support Groups
- Parent-infant Therapeutic Group — helping parents enjoy their relationship with their baby or toddler
- individual therapy — provided on a limited basis to women on the waiting list or attending the group program
- community education seminars to promote knowledge and awareness of the mental health needs of parents and their babies.

WA Perinatal Mental Health Unit
www.wnhs.health.wa.gov.au/wapmhu.php (for health professionals)
www.wnhs.health.wa.gov.au/emotionalhealth.php (for consumers)
The Western Australian Perinatal Mental Health Unit (WAPMHU) is a non-clinical unit based at King Edward Memorial Hospital in Subiaco. The unit provides information for consumers and health professionals on the mental health of parents and families during the perinatal period. The website for consumers is very useful. The health professionals' website explains the work of WAPMHU in the areas of research, coordination of existing service providers, improving services (especially in the area of Indigenous and CALD perinatal mental health) and finally in education, training and health promotion.

Mother Baby Unit
08 9340 1799
Free call 1800 422 588
www.kemh.health.wa.gov.au/services/mbu/index.htm
11 Loretto St, Subiaco WA 6008
The Mother and Baby Unit (MBU) functions as a state-wide inpatient treatment centre for acute perinatal psychiatric conditions. A part of the Women and Newborn Health Service, the Mother Baby Unit is located adjacent to King Edward Memorial Hospital for Women (KEMH).

Women and their babies 0–12 months may be admitted to the inpatient program if they have significant mental health problems following the birth of a baby. These include: severe depression, anxiety or a psychotic illness such as a bipolar mood disorder or schizophrenia.
The eight bed, free-standing unit situated in Subiaco includes:

- eight single rooms with ensuite
- facilities for partners to stay when appropriate
- a nursery and sleep rooms for babies when they are not rooming-in

- a laundry
- a kitchen and milk preparation kitchen
- several living rooms.

Referrals are accepted from any health professional.

Parenting support and resources

The Parenting Line
086279 1200
1800 654 432 (freecall for STD callers)
24 hours, 7 days a week
The Parenting Line is a telephone information service for parents and carers with children from birth to 18 years. Qualified staff can answers questions and provide resources and advice on all issues relating to parenting including health, behaviour and family relationships.

NGALA Family Resource Centre & Helpline
08 9368 9368 (Helpline)
1800 111 546 (Country Access)
www.ngala.com.au
7 days, 8am to 8pm
Ngala supports families with young children from babies to school age. There are several centres throughout the state offering parent groups, individual consultations and day and overnight stay facilities. An in-home visiting service is a new addition to Ngala.

There are many, many types of parent groups and workshops including several for dads, sleep, newborns, toileting and many more. Ngala also produces books, DVDs, tip sheets and resource guides.

Ngala runs workshops all over the state. A helpline can be accessed by all WA residents and the excellent website can, of course, be accessed by all Australians.

Parenting WA
08 6279 1200
1800 654 432 (freecall for STD callers)
28 Alvan Street, Mount Lawley WA 6050
24 hours, 7 days a week
Parenting library
08 6279 1223
1800 686 155 (freecall for STD callers)
www.communities.wa.gov.au/childrenandfamilies/parentingwa

Parenting WA provides a broad range of parenting advice and support across the whole of WA. The staff are highly trained and can do home visits as well as providing consultations at the centre. Parenting coordinators are situated all around the state and details can be found on the website or by calling the centre. A parenting library can post out books as well as being visited in person. The Parenting Line is also run by Parenting WA.

CLAN WA
08 9228 9006
www.clanwa.com.au
335 Pier Street, East Perth WA 6004
CLAN WA has five local offices throughout Perth and aims to assist families in building resilience. Paid staff and trained volunteers work alongside families and communities, using one-to-one visits and short courses as well as community events to offer support and information. Issues of parenting, isolation, mental illness and relationships can be discussed.

Good Beginnings
0438 800 914 (National Programs Coordinator)
www.goodbeginnings.org.au
Good Beginnings offers programs designed to assist families with young children. Call their offices to ask for more information on what is currently available.

Becoming a Parent: Emotional Health and Wellbeing
This booklet contains practical advice for parents and helps them adjust to the emotional issues surrounding childbirth. It is usually given out at antenatal appointments, and can also be downloaded from:
www.wnhs.health.wa.gov.au/emotionalhealth.php.

The Best For Me and My Baby
This *booklet* was developed with, and for, women with a mental health problem or mental illness — and their partners — who are thinking about having a baby, are new parents or are about to have a baby. It encourages health professionals and parents to work together to manage mental health during pregnancy and early parenthood and provides tips for parents and for supporting family *and* friends. It is available from www.copmi.net.au/common/download.html#resource in
the following community languages: Hindi, Chinese, Dinka, Swahili, Spanish and Arabic.

Men's support and resources

Hey Dad WA
08 9368 9368 (metro callers)
1800 111 546 (country callers)
www.ngala.com.au (follow links to 'Ngala and You' and 'In The Community')
The Hey Dad WA team at Ngala provides a 'male friendly' environment across all Ngala services. Hey Dad WA is particularly involved in Ngala's fathering workshops and learning sessions as well as in some antenatal and postnatal depression support programs. Mums and dads are welcome to call the team to ask about information and resources on all aspects of fatherhood.

Dads in the Early Years
www.meerilinga.org.au/Parenting
Resources just for dads are found on this family-friendly website.

Multicultural services

West Australian Transcultural Mental Health Service
08 9224 1760
www.mmha.org.au/wamhc
5 Murray Street, Perth, WA 6000
A state-wide tertiary service designed to meet the mental health needs of people from culturally and linguistically diverse (CALD) backgrounds.

Family and carer support

Carers WA
1300 227 377
www.wa.carersaustralia.com.au
182 Lord Street, Perth WA 6000
Carers WA provides counselling, advice, advocacy, education and training to carers. The National Carer Counselling Program is managed by Carers WA. Carers can receive six free counselling sessions from a professionally trained and qualified counsellor either in person or by telephone. More general telephone support and counselling is available at any time on the telephone number above.

ARAFMI Mental Health Carers & Friends Association (WA)
08 9427 7100

www.arafmi.asn.au

ARAFMI offers free family support counselling at its offices around Perth and in rural regions. Telephone counselling is also available. ARAFMI also provides advocacy and information services on mental illness.

Other state helplines

Crisis Care Helpline
08 9223 1111
1800 199 008 (country callers)
24 hours, 7 days a week
Crisis Care can help you find solutions to acute problems of all sorts. Referrals, advice, support and counselling are provided.

BOOKS ON PERINATAL DEPRESSION AND ANXIETY

There are many books on anxiety and depression around childbirth, mainly from the USA, and a full list would be quite overwhelming we feel. So we have included here a list of books and blogs which we think are the best, the most helpful and useful.

Beyond the Blues, A Guide to Understanding and Treating Prenatal and Postpartum Depression
Shoshana Bennett and Pec Indman
2011 new edition
An easy-to-read guide; particularly helpful for people living with, or caring for, a woman with a perinatal mood disorder.

Down came the rain. A mother's story of depression and recovery
Brooke Shields
2005 Penguin Books Australia
Open and honest account of Brooke Shields experience of depression after the birth of her child.

Preventing the Bough from Breaking: Overcoming Postnatal Depression
2008 Family Support Network Inc, Lismore, NSW, 2480

This book and DVD program has been developed by professionals with years of experience researching and working with women suffering perinatal anxiety and depression. The chapters can be worked through individually or with a health professional.

Postnatal Depression: A practical guide for Australian families
Lisa Fettling
2002 IP Communications
www.lisafettling.com.au
A straightforward and compassionate account of postnatal depression, outdated in some ways but well worth reading.

Postpartum Depression for Dummies
Shoshanna S Bennett
2007 Wiley Publishing, Inc
Not all books in the Dummies series are created equal, but this is a good one. It covers almost everything you need to know, but with an American focus.

Pregnant on Prozac: The Essential Guide to Making the Best Decision for You and Your Baby
Shoshanna S Bennett
2009 GPP Life
A warm and useful book by the busy Dr Bennett, covering the neglected side of perinatal mood disorders — antenatal anxiety and depression. Whilst the focus is on antidepressants it also covers talking therapies and alternative treatments.

Women's Experience of Postnatal Depression: Kitchen table conversations
Lisa Fettling and Belinda Tune
2005 IP Communications
www.lisafettling.com.au
Personal stories of Australian women who have experienced and recovered from postnatal anxiety and depression. This book provides insights into the struggles and challenges faced by these women and their families, and the strategies they used in their recovery.

This Isn't What I Expected: Overcoming Postpartum Depression
Karen Kleiman and Valerie Raskin
1994 Bantam
An informative and practical guide. Although it is somewhat dated there is still plenty of relevant information and practical ideas.

Treating Postnatal Depression: A psychological Approach for Health Care Professionals
Jeannette Milgrom, Paul Martin & Lisa Negri
2003, reprinted 2006 Wiley
A thorough guide, not intended for the lay reader, but invaluable for professionals.

My Journey to Her World : How I Coped with My Wife's Depression
Michael Lurie
2007 Grosvenor House
www.mypartnersdepression.com
A very honest account of how one father helped his wife as she recovered from depression.

The Yellow Wallpaper
Charlotte Perkins Gilman
1892, Small and Maynard
 www.amazon.com
An American writer's short story, one of the earliest literary accounts of postnatal depression.

General depression books

Black Dog Books
The Black Dog Institute in Sydney publishes several general books on depression and other mood disorders, have a look at their list at:
www.blackdoginstitute.org.au/aboutus/blackdogbooks.cfm

Back from the Brink: Australians tell their Stories of overcoming Depression
Back From The Brink Too, Helping Your Loved One Overcome Depression
Graeme Cowan
2007 Bird in Hand Media
www.graemecowan.com.au
A popular book with many stories of treatment and recovery from depression of all types, read for inspiration.

Books on being a parent

Buddhism for Mothers, a calm approach to caring for yourself and your children
Buddhism For Mothers of Young Children

Buddhism for Mothers of School Children
Sarah Napthali
2004 onwards Allen and Unwin
The wisdom of Buddhism applied to motherhood and the author's honest descriptions of her struggles and successes in applying it.

The Mask of Motherhood: How mothering changes everything and why we pretend it doesn't
Susan Maushart
1997 Random House
A sociologist's view of some of the many tensions facing modern mothers. In an accessible and thought provoking book motherhood is cleverly dissected and analysed (with a degree of irony) leading to some thought provoking conclusions.

Mother Me: a mum's guide to balance, wellbeing and harmony
Karen Brown
2008 Pan Macmillan
A practical workbook full of ideas and insights on many aspects of motherhood.

Kidwrangling: Caring for Babies, Toddlers and Preschoolers
Kaz Cooke
2010 Penguin Australia
www.kazcooke.com.au
www.penguin.com.au/kidwrangling/
Kaz Cooke's lighthearted and humorous take on parenting, a companion to her Up The Duff book on pregnancy.

Staying Mum: What your Mum forgot to tell you and your best friends never dared
Mara Lee
2010 John Wiley and Sons
A lighthearted anecdotal tale of one woman's experience of motherhood.

Towards Parenthood: Preparing for the changes and challenges of a new baby
Jeannette Milgrom et al
2009 ACER Press
www.acerpress.com.au
A workbook prepared by the Parent-Infant Research Institute which deals with caring for yourself, and your relationship as well as with a new baby.

GLOSSARY

Adjustment disorder: A mental health disorder resulting from difficulty adapting to stressors.

Antenatal: The period between conception and birth. Sometimes called prenatal.

Anticonvulsants: Medications used in the treatment of epilepsy. Many anticonvulsants also act as mood stabilisers and are used in the treatment of bipolar disorder.

Antidepressants: Medications used to treat mood disorders, such as major depression. Antidepressants include tricyclic antidepressants (TCAs), selective serotonin reuptake inhibitors (SSRIs) and serotonin noradrenaline reuptake inhibitors (SNRIs).

Antipsychotics: A group of medications primarily used to manage psychosis, particularly in schizophrenia and bipolar disorder.

Behaviour/al therapy: Psychological therapy that focuses on training individuals to replace undesirable behaviours with healthier ones.

Benzodiazepines: A class of medicines used to treat anxiety and bring about sleep.

Bipolar disorder: A mental health disorder, previously called manic depression, which is characterised by mood swings between great energy (mania) and depression.

Bright light therapy: Light therapy is a way to treat seasonal affective disorder (SAD) and other forms of depression, by exposure to artificial light.

Care pathway: A multidisciplinary plan for delivering health and social care to patients with a specific condition or set of symptoms, with the aim of supporting continuity of care.

Cleft palate: Incomplete development of the roof of the mouth.

Clinical trial: A research study conducted with patients which tests out a medication or other intervention, to assess its effectiveness and safety.

Cognitive: Pertaining to cognition, the process of being aware, knowing, thinking, learning and judging.

Cognitive-behaviour/al therapy: A psychological therapy which combines cognitive and behavioural therapy techniques. Treatment focuses on changing an individual's thoughts (cognitive patterns) and/or problem behaviours in order to change emotional states.

Cognitive therapy: A psychological therapy based on the belief that psychological problems are the product of faulty ways of thinking about the world. The aim of cognitive therapy is to teach people to become aware of these thinking patterns and change them. This process is called cognitive restructuring.

DSM: Abbreviation for the *Diagnostic and Statistical Manual of Mental Disorders*, a comprehensive classification of officially recognised psychiatric disorders, published by the American Psychiatric Association, for use by mental health professionals to ensure uniformity of diagnosis. DSM-IV designates the 4th edition.

Edinburgh Postnatal Depression Scale (EPDS): The most commonly used screening tool for depression during the perinatal period, called the *Edinburgh Depression Scale* (EDS) when used during pregnancy.

Electroconvulsive therapy (ECT): A therapy for severely depressed patients in which a brief electric current is sent through the brain of an anaesthetised patient.

Evidenced-based: Refers to the use of best evidence derived from methodologically rigorous, valid research.

Folate: A B vitamin that is essential for cell growth and reproduction; also called *folic acid*.

Generalised anxiety disorder (GAD): A mental health disorder characterised by persistent, excessive anxiety and worry.

Infant attachment therapy: Therapy which focuses on building a secure emotional attachment between the child and caregiver.

Interpersonal therapy: A short-term psychological therapy that focuses on the connection between a patient's relationships with peers and family members and their psychological disorder symptoms.

Mental health disorder: Diagnosed disorder (depression, anxiety disorder, bipolar disorder, puerperal psychosis), which may be mild, moderate or severe.

Mindfulness: A meditative state of enhanced awareness and non-judgemental attention.

Mood disorder: A collection of disorders characterised by major disruptions in patients' moods and emotions; includes major depression and bipolar disorder.

Mood stabilisers: Medications used to treat mood disorders, such as bipolar disorder.

Neonate: A newborn infant; one less than four weeks old.

Neurotransmitter: A chemical messenger in the nervous system that permit nerve cells to communicate eg dopamine, serotonin and noradrenaline.

Obsessive compulsive disorder (OCD): An anxiety disorder in which an individual experiences recurrent unwanted thoughts or rituals that they cannot control.

Omega-3 fatty acids: Essential fatty acids commonly found in certain fish oils including salmon and other cold-water fish.

Panic disorder: An anxiety disorder characterised by short lived, sudden attacks of terror and fear of losing control.

Perinatal period: The period covering pregnancy and the first year following pregnancy or childbirth.

Phobia: An anxiety disorder characterised by extreme and irrational fear of simple things or social situations.

Posttraumatic stress disorder (PTSD): An anxiety disorder that may develop in response to exposure to one or more traumatic events.

Preeclampsia: A complication of pregnancy characterised by high blood pressure, protein in the urine, and swelling (oedema) due to fluid retention.

Preterm birth: A baby born before 37 weeks of pregnancy; also called premature birth.

Prevalence: The total number of cases of a disease in a given population at a specific time.

Psychodynamic therapy: A psychological therapy that places greater emphasis on the influence of past experience on the development of current behaviour and emotions, mediated in part through unconscious processes. The approach focuses on gaining insight into these and developing strategies for change.

Psychosis: A severe mental health disorder in which contact with reality is lost or highly distorted.

Psychosocial: Pertaining to a combination of psychological and social factors.

Psychosocial assessment: Broad clinical evaluation of medical, psychological and social history and current status, including risk and protective factors.

Psychotherapy: A general term that refers to non-medical treatment for psychological issues.

Puerperal psychosis: A serious mental health disorder associated with the sudden onset of psychotic symptoms following childbirth.

Risk factor: An aspect of a person's condition, lifestyle or environment that increases the probability of occurrence of a disease or condition.

S-Adenosyl Methionine (SAMe): A dietary supplement used for the treatment of depression, arthritic pain and inflammation

Schizophrenia: A mental health disorder characterised by psychotic behaviour, bizarre thought processes and paranoia

Screening: The examination of a group of usually asymptomatic individuals to detect those with a high probability of having or developing a given disease/ disorder.

St Johns's wort: A herbal remedy from the flowering plant, *Hypericum perforatum*, used in the treatment of depression.

Supportive counselling: A counselling approach where a health professional discusses options and choices with a patient, without imposing their own views or values about what the patient should do; sometimes called *non-directive counselling*.

REFERENCES

CHAPTER 2

1. Bennett SS (2007) *Postpartum Depression for Dummies*. Indianapolis: Wiley Publishing Inc.

2. *beyondblue* Guidelines Expert Advisory Committee (2010) *Clinical practice guidelines for depression and related disorders — anxiety, bipolar disorder and puerperal psychosis — in the perinatal period*. A guideline for health professionals providing care in the perinatal period. www.beyondblue.org.au/index.aspx?link_id=6.1246&tmp=FileDownlo ad&fid=1626 (accessed April 2010).

3. American Psychiatric Association (APA) (2000) *Diagnostic and Statistical Manual of Mental Disorders: DSM IV*. 4th edition — Text Revision. Washington DC: American Psychiatric Association.

4. Austin MP, Priest S, Hadzi-Pavlovic D, et al (2010) Depressive and Anxiety Disorders in the postpartum period: what is their prevalence and can we improve on their detection? *Archives of Womens Mental Health* 13: 395–401.

5. Williams L, Jacka F, Pasco J, et al. (2010) The prevalence of mood and anxiety disorders in Australian women. *Australasian Psychiatry* 18: 250–255.

Additional references:

Barnett B, Glossop P, Haling M (2008) *Caring for the Family's Future. A Practical Guide to Identification and Management of Perinatal Anxiety and Depression*. 4th edition. Sydney: Surry Beatty & Sons.

Black Dog Institute (2009) *Biochemical causes of depression*. www.blackdoginstitute.org.au/ docs/BiochemicalCausesOfDepression.pdf (accessed June 2010).

Buist A (2008) *Perinatal depression — Where are we in 2008?* Online article for Swinburne Institute: http://ojs.lib.swin.edu.au/index.php/ejap/article/view/131/132 (accessed July 2010).

Calabresi L (2010) Perinatal depression, in *Australian Doctor Mental Health Seminar Report*, June 2010: 4–5.

Fettling L (2002) *Postnatal Depression. A Practical Guide for Australian Families*. Melbourne: IP Communications.

McKay D (2010) Perinatal depression. *Australian Doctor* 30 April 2010: 27–34.

Musters C, McDonald E, Jones I (2008) Management of postnatal depression. *BMJ* 337: 399–403.

New Zealand Guidelines Group (2008) *Identification of Common Mental Disorders and Management of Depression in Primary Care. An Evidence-based Best Practice Guideline*. New

Zealand Guidelines Group, Wellington.

NICE (2007) *Antenatal and postnatal mental health: Clinical management and service guidance.* The British Psychological Society & Royal College of Psychiatrists. www.nice.org.uk.CG45 (accessed November 2009).

Post and Antenatal Depression Association (PANDA) Inc (2010) Fact Sheet 2. Antenatal depression.   www.panda.org.au/images/stories/PDFs/Antenatal_Depression.pdf   (accessed June 2010).

Ryan D, Milis L, Misri N (2005) Depression during pregnancy. *Canadian Family Physician* 51: 1087–1093.

CHAPTER 3

1. Forty L, Jones L, Macgregor S, et al (2006) Familiarity of postpartum depression in unipolar disorder: results of a family study. *American Journal of Psychiatry* 163: 1549–1553.

2. Bloch M, Schmidt PJ, Danaceau M, et al (2000) Effects of gonadal steroids in women with a history of postpartum depression. *American Journal of Psychiatry* 157: 924–930.

3. *beyondblue* Guidelines Expert Advisory Committee (2010) *Clinical practice guidelines for depression and related disorders — anxiety, bipolar disorder and puerperal psychosis — in the perinatal period.* A guideline for health professionals providing care in the perinatal period. www.beyondblue.org.au/index.aspx?link_id=6.1246&tmp=FileDownload&fid=1626 (accessed April 2010).

Additional references:

Barnett B, Glossop P, Haling M (2008) *Caring for the Family's Future. A Practical Guide to Identification and Management of Perinatal Anxiety and Depression.* 4th edition. Sydney: Surry Beatty & Sons.

Buist A (2008) *Perinatal depression — Where are we in 2008?* Online article for Swinburne Institute:ojs.lib.swin.edu.au/index.php/ejap/article/view/131/132 (accessed July 2010).

Calabresi L (2010) Perinatal depression, in *Australian Doctor Mental Health Seminar Report*, June 2010: 4–5.

Fettling L (2002) *Postnatal Depression. A Practical Guide for Australian Families.* Melbourne: IP Communications.

McKay D (2010) Perinatal depression. *Australian Doctor* 30 April 2010: 27–34.

Musters C, McDonald E, Jones I (2008) Management of postnatal depression. *BMJ* 337: 399–403.

New Zealand Guidelines Group (2008) *Identification of Common Mental Disorders and Management of Depression in Primary Care. An Evidence-based Best Practice Guideline.* Wellington: New Zealand Guidelines Group.

NICE (2007) *Antenatal and postnatal mental health: Clinical management and service guidance.* The British Psychological Society & Royal College of Psychiatrists. www.nice.org.uk.CG45 (accessed November 2009).

Pearlstein T (2008) Perinatal depression: treatment options and dilemmas. *Journal of Psychiatry & Neuroscience* 33: 302–308.

Ryan D, Milis L, Misri N (2005) Depression during pregnancy. *Canadian Family Physician* 51: 1087–1093.

CHAPTER 4

1. Kendell RE, Chalmers JC, Platz C (1987) Epidemiology of puerperal psychoses. *British Journal of Psychiatry* 150: 662–673.

2. Austin MP (2004) Antenatal screening and early intervention for "perinatal" distress, depression and anxiety: where to from here? *Archive of Women's Mental Health* 7:1–6.

3. *beyondblue National Postnatal Depression Program* VOL I: National Screening Program 2001–2005 This report was prepared by A/Prof Anne Buist and Dr Justin Bilszta (National Director and National Project Manager).

4. Cox JL, Holden JM and Sagovsky R (1987) Detection of postnatal depression. Development of the 10-item Edinburgh Postnatal Depression Scale. *The British Journal of Psychiatry* 150: 782–786.

5. Milgrom J, Leigh B (2007) Acceptability of antenatal screening for depression in routine antenatal care. *Australian Journal of Advanced Nursing* 24(3): 14–18.

6. Mathey, S (2009) Are we overpathologising motherhood? Journal of Affective Disorders doi:10.1016/j.jad.2009.05.004.

7. Bria K (2008). *Conference presentation*. Preventing the Bough from Breaking; New Approaches to postnatal depression, Bonding and Attachment. Byron Bay, 28 – 29 April 2008

Additional references:
beyondblue National Action Plan for Perinatal Mental Health 2008–2010: Full Report..

CHAPTER 5

1. NICE (2007) *Antenatal and postnatal mental health: Clinical management and service guidance*. The British Psychological Society & Royal College of Psychiatrists. www.nice.org.uk.CG45 (accessed November 2009).

2. American Psychiatric Association (APA) (2000) *Diagnostic and Statistical Manual of Mental Disorders*: DSM IV. 4th edition. Washington DC: American Psychiatric Association.

3. Barnett B, Glossop P, Haling M (2008) *Caring for the Family's Future. A Practical Guide to Identification and Management of Perinatal Anxiety and Depression*. 4th edition. Sydney: Surry Beatty & Sons.

4. Austin MP, Priest S, Hadzi-Pavlovic D, et al (2010) Depressive and Anxiety Disorders in the postpartum period: what is their prevalence and can we improve on their detection? *Archives of Women's Mental Health* 13: 395-401.

5. Pearson A (2010) *Depression's the curse of my generation and I'm struggling in its grasp*. Mail Online April 28 2010 www.dailymail.co.uk/femail/article-1269376/Depressions-curse-generation-Im-struggling-grasp.html#ixzz0mNoJ6ZyE (accessed April 2010).

Additional references:
Bennett SS, Indman P (2006) *Beyond the Blues. A Guide to Understanding and Treating Prenatal and Postpartum Depression*. 2nd edition. San Jose, CA: Moodswings Press.

beyondblue Guidelines Expert Advisory Committee (2010) *Clinical practice guidelines for depression and related disorders — anxiety, bipolar disorder and puerperal psychosis — in the perinatal period*. A guideline for health professionals providing care in the perinatal period. www.beyondblue.org.au/index.aspx?link_id=6.1246&tmp=FileDownload&fid=1626 (accessed April 2010).

Fettling L (2002) *Postnatal Depression. A Practical Guide for Australian Families*. Melbourne: IP Communications.

McKay D. (2010) Perinatal depression. *Australian Doctor* 30April 2010: 27–34.

CHAPTER 6

1. *beyondblue* Guidelines Expert Advisory Committee (2010) *Clinical practice guidelines for depression and related disorders — anxiety, bipolar disorder and puerperal psychosis — in the perinatal period*. A guideline for health professionals providing care in the perinatal period. www.beyondblue.org.au/index.aspx?link_id=6.1246&tmp=FileDownload&fid=1626 (accessed April 2010).

2. Bilszta J, Erickse J, Buist A, Milgrom J (2006) *Optimising Emotional Health during Pregnancy and Early Parenthood. Improving Access to Help for Women with Perinatal Depression*. Final Report to the *beyondblue* Victorian Centre for Excellence in Depression and Related Disorders. 15th October 2005–1st September 2006.

3. Austin M-P, Frilingos M, Lumley J, et al (2008) Brief antenatal cognitive behaviour therapy group intervention for the prevention of postnatal depression and anxiety: A randomized controlled trial. *Journal of Affective Disorders* 105: 35–44.

4. Dennis CL, Hodnett ED (2007) Psychosocial and psychological interventions for treating postpartum depression. *Cochrane Database of Systematic Reviews* 2007, Issue 4. Art No: CD006116. DOI: 10.1002/14651858.CD006116.pub2.

5. Stewart RE, Chambless DL (2009) Cognitive-behavioral therapy for adult anxiety disorders in clinical practice: a meta-analysis of effectiveness studies. *Journal of Consulting and Clinical Psychology* 77:4: 595-606.

6. Dennis CL, Hodnett E, Kenton L, et al (2009) Effect of peer support on prevention of postnatal depression among high risk women: multisite randomised controlled trial. *BMJ* 338:a306

7. Bowlby J (1969) *Attachment and Loss, Volume 1: Attachment*. London: Hogarth Press and the Institute of Psychoanalysis.

8. Bowlby J (1973) *Attachment and Loss, Volume 2: Separation: Anxiety and Anger*. London: Hogarth Press and the Institute of Psychoanalysis.

9. Bowlby J (1980) *Attachment and Loss, Volume 3: Loss: Sadness and Depression*. London: Hogarth Press and the Institute of Psychoanalysis.

10. Karen R (1998) *Becoming Attached. First relationships and how they shape our capacity to love*. New York: Oxford University Press

11. Cohen N, Muir E, Lojkasek M, Muir R, Parker C, Barwick M, Brown M (1999) Watch, wait and wonder: testing the effectiveness of a new approach to mother-infant psychotherapy. *Infant Mental Health Journal* 20, 429–451.

Additional references:

Bennett SS (2007) *Postpartum Depression for Dummies*. Indianapolis: Wiley Publishing Inc.

Cooper PJ, Murray L, Wilson A, Romaniuk H (2003) Controlled trial of the short- and long-term effect of psychological treatment of post-partum depression. British *Journal of Psychiatry* 182: 412–419.

Freeman MP, Fava M, Lake J, et al (2010) Complementary and Alternative Medicine in Major Depressive Disorder: the American Psychiatric Association Task Force Assessment of Evidence, Challenges and Recommendations. *Journal of Clinical Psychiatry* 71: 669–681.

From the Heart WA (2010) *Write from the Heart. Personal Stories of Perinatal Depression and Anxiety*. 3rd edition. From the Heart WA Inc. 2010.

Holden JM, Sagovsky R, Cox JL (1989) Counselling in a general practice setting: controlled study of health visitor intervention in treatment of postnatal depression. *BMJ* 298: 223–6.

Hunot V, Churchill R, Teixeira V, Silva de Lima M (2007) Psychological therapies for generalised anxiety disorder. *Cochrane Database of Systematic Reviews* 2007, Issue 1. Art No: CD001848. DOI: 10.1002/14651858.CD001848.pub4.

Musters C, McDonald E, Jones I (2008) Management of postnatal depression. *BMJ* 337: 399–403.

NICE (2007) Antenatal and postnatal mental health: Clinical management and service guidance. The British Psychological Society & Royal College of Psychiatrists. Available from: www.nice.org.uk.CG45 (accessed November 2009).

Parker G, Parker I, Brotchie H, Stuart S (2006) Interpersonal psychotherapy for depression? The need to define its ecological niche. *Journal of Affective Disorders* 95: 1–11.

Reavley N, Allen N, Jorm A, Morgan A, Purcell R (2010) *A Guide to What Works for Anxiety Disorders*. *beyondblue*: Melbourne.

Reavley N, Allen N, Jorm A, Morgan A, Purcell R (2009) *A Guide to What Works for Depression*. *beyondblue*: Melbourne.

Spinelli MG, Endicott J (2003) Controlled clinical trial of interpersonal psychotherapy versus parenting education program for depressed pregnant woman. *American Journal of Psychiatry* 160: 555-562.

CHAPTER 7

1. Calabresi L (2010) Perinatal depression. *Australian Doctor Mental Health Seminar Report* June: 4–5.

2. *beyondblue* Guidelines Expert Advisory Committee (2010) *Clinical practice guidelines for depression and related disorders — anxiety, bipolar disorder and puerperal psychosis — in the perinatal period*. A guideline for health professionals providing care in the perinatal period. www.beyondblue.org.au/index.aspx?link_id=6.1246&tmp=FileDownload&fid=1626 (accessed April 2010).

3. McKay D (2010) Perinatal depression. *Australian Doctor* 30 April 2010: 27–34.

4. Frayne J, Nguyen T, Allen S (2009) Motherhood and mental illness. Part 2 — Management and medications. *Australian Family Physician* 38: 688–692.

5. Australian Medicines Handbook Pty Ltd (2010) *Australian Medicines Handbook* (AMH).

6. Pearlstein T, Howard M, Salisbury A, Zlotnick C (2009) Postpartum depression. *American Journal of Obstetrics and Gynecology* 200: 357–364.

7. NICE (2007) *Antenatal and postnatal mental health: Clinical management and service guidance*. The British Psychological Society & Royal College of Psychiatrists. Available from: www.nice.org.uk.CG45 (accessed November 2009).

8. Freeman MP, Fava M, Lake J, et al (2010) Complementary and Alternative Medicine in Major Depressive Disorder: the American Psychiatric Association Task Force Assessment of Evidence, Challenges and Recommendations. *Journal of Clinical Psychiatry* 71: 669–681.

9. Food Standards Australia New Zealand. *Mercury in Fish*. Consumer Information. www.

foodstandards.gov.au/consumerinformation/adviceforpregnantwomen/mercuryinfish.cfm (accessed October 2010).

10. Bennett SS (2009) *Pregnant on Prozac. The Essential Guide to Making the Best Decision for You and Your Baby*. Guildford, CT, USA: GPP Life.

11. New Zealand Guidelines Group (2008) *Identification of Common Mental Disorders and Management of Depression in Primary Care*. An Evidence-based Best Practice Guideline. Wellington: New Zealand Guidelines Group.

Additional references:

Agency for Healthcare Research and Quality (2002) *S-Adenosyl-L-Methionine (SAMe) for Depression, Osteoarthritis, and Liver Disease, Structured Abstract*. Agency for Healthcare Research and Quality, Rockville, MD. www.ahrq.gov/clinic/tp/sametp.htm (accessed October 2010).

Bennett SS, Indman P (2006) *Beyond the Blues. A Guide to Understanding and Treating Prenatal and Postpartum Depression*. 2nd edition. San Jose, CA: Moodswings Press.

Bennett SS (2007) *Postpartum Depression for Dummies*. Indianapolis: Wiley Publishing Inc.

Fettling L (2002) Postnatal Depression. *A Practical Guide for Australian Families*. Melbourne: IP Communications.

Food Standards Australia New Zealand. *Folic acid/Folate*. Consumer Information. www.foodstandards.gov.au/consumerinformation/adviceforpregnantwomen/folicacidfolateandpr4598.cfm (accessed October 2010).

Pearlstein T (2008) Perinatal depression: treatment options and dilemmas. *Journal of Psychiatry & Neuroscience* 33: 302–308.

CHAPTER 9

1. Paulson JF, Dauber S, Leiferman J (2006) Individual and Combined Effects of Postpartum Depression in Mothers and Fathers on Parenting. *Behavior Pediatrics* 118(2):659–668 (doi:10.1542/peds.2005-2948).

2. Milgrom J, Martin P, Negri L (1999) *Treating Postnatal Depression: A Psychological Approach for Health Care Practitioners*. Chichester: John Wiley and Sons.

3. Fletcher RJ, Matthey S, Marley CG (2006) Addressing Depression and Anxiety among new fathers. *Medical Journal of Australia* 185: 461–463.

4. Meighan M, Davis MW, Thomas SP, Droppleman PG (1999) Living with postpartum depression. The father's experience. *American Journal of Maternal Child Nursing* 2494: 202–208.

5. Condon JT, Boyce P, Corkindale C (2004) The first time father's study: a prospective study of the mental health and wellbeing of men during the transition to parenthood. *Australian and New Zealand Journal of Psychiatry* 38(1–2): 56–64.

6. Ballard P (2008) Fathers: Bringing them into the picture. In S Williams and V Cowling (eds). *Infants of parents with mental illness*. Bowen Hills: Australian Academic Press.

CHAPTER 10

1. Choi Y, Bishai, Minkovitz CS (2009) Multiple births are a risk factor for postpartum maternal depressive symptoms. *Pediatrics* 123: 1147–1154.

2. Vigood SN, Villegas L, Ross LE (2010) Prevalence and risk factors for postpartum

depression among women with preterm and low birth weight infants: a systematic review. *BJOG* 117: 540–550.

3. Miller LJ (2002) Postpartum depression. *JAMA* 287: 762–765.

4. Laws P and Sullivan EA (2009) *Australia's mothers and babies 2007*. Perinatal statistics series no 23. Cat no PER 48. Sydney: AIHW National Perinatal Statistics Unit.

5. Condon JT (1986) Management of established pathological grief reaction after stillbirth. *American Journal of Psychiatry* 143: 987–992.

6. Hughes PM, Turton P, Evans CDH (1999) Stillbirth as risk factor for depression and anxiety in the subsequent pregnancy: cohort study. *BMJ* 318: 1721–1724.

7. Bennett SS (2007) *Postpartum Depression for Dummies*. Indianapolis: Wiley Publishing Inc.

CHAPTER 11

1. Cooper PJ, Murray L. (1995) Course and recurrence of postnatal depression. Evidence for the specificity of the diagnostic concept. *British Journal of Psychiatry* 166: 191–195.

2. Post and Antenatal Depression Association Inc. Fact Sheet 7: *Having another baby after depression*. www.panda.org.au.

3. Cohen LS, Altshuler LL, Harlow BL, et al (2006) Relapse of major depression during pregnancy in women who maintain or discontinue antidepressant treatment. *JAMA* 295: 499–507.

4. Viguera AC, Nonacs R, Cohen LS, et al (2000) Risk of Recurrence of bipolar disorder in pregnant and nonpregnant women after discontinuing lithium maintenance. *American Journal of Psychiatry* 157: 179–184.

5. Bennett SS (2007) *Postpartum Depression for Dummies*. Indianapolis: Wiley Publishing Inc.

Additional references:
Calabresi L (2010) Perinatal depression, in *Australian Doctor Mental Health Seminar Report* June: 4–5.

Dennis CL, Creedy DK (2004) Psychosocial and psychological interventions for preventing postpartum depression. *Cochrane Database of Systematic Reviews*, Issue 4. Art No: CD001134. DOI: 10.1002/14651858.CD001134.pub2.

Fettling L(2002) *Postnatal Depression. A Practical Guide for Australian Families*. Melbourne: IP Communications.

J Frayne J, Nguyen T, Allen S (2009) Motherhood and mental illness. Part 1 — toward a general understanding. *Australian Family Physician* August 2009: 594–597.

Musters C, McDonald E, Jones I (2008) Management of postnatal depression. *BMJ* 337: 399–340.References:

CHAPTER 15

Maushart S (1999) *The Mask of Motherhood; How becoming a mother changes everything and why we pretend it doesn't*. New York: New Press.

INDEX

health professionals
    accessing 249–50
    advice for families and friends 205–7
    diagnostic assessment methods 84–6, 87–8
    psychiatrists 101
    psychologists 100, 147
    support from 248–9
    talking to 262–5
helplines, national 275–8
hormonal sensitivity 47
hospitalisation 109–11, 154–5, 218–20

identity, changes in 19–20, 137
infant attachment therapy 111
information 90, 92–4, 166, 217, 278–80
    conflicting sources 92
    need for 261
    quality 93–4, 130
    resources *see* resources guide
    talking and 252–7
interpersonal psychotherapy (IPT) 98
isolated mothers 248
isolation 12–13, 15, 27, 106, 153
    cultural 50

judgemental comments 19, 233

Lifeline 44, 276, 282

magnetic resonance imaging (MRI) 29
management plan 91
Maushart, Susan
    The Mask of Motherhood 256–7
Medicare
    assistance 284–5
    Better Access to Mental Health Care scheme
        90, 99, 285
    registration of counsellors 102
medications 90, 114–16, 150–1, 250, 282–3
    antidepressants 117–25
    antipsychotics 126–7
    benzodiazepines 126
    breastfeeding 115
    failure to take 115–16
    mood stabilisers 126
    pregnancy, during 33–4, 115
mental health
    internet-based programs 283–4
    multicultural 282
Mindfulness Based Cognitive Therapy (MBCT)
97
miscarriage 54, 137, 148, 191–3
mood changes 30
mood disorder 29

mood stabilisers 126
MoodGYM 97, 283–4
mother baby units (MBUs) 142, 143–4
Motherisk 121, 283
mothers
    attitudes to 14–15
    conspiracy of silence 253, 256–9
    early intervention 72–3
    guilt 235–6
    isolated 248
    myths 17
    performance anxiety 256
    pressures from society 253–5
    self-help strategies 234–51
    single 248
    teenage 51–2
multiple births 54–5, 157–60, 183–8

neonatal death 54, 191–3
    support organisations 193
neurotransmitters 29
'normality' 23
NSW Multicultural Health Communication
Service 50, 295–6

obsessive compulsive disorder (OCD) 31, 38, 79
occupational therapists 102–3
Occupational Therapy Australia 103
OCD *see* obsessive compulsive disorder (OCD)
31
Omega-3 fatty acids 131–2

PANDA 82, 101, 102, 106, 110, 122, 141, 146,
180, 203, 207, 209, 215, 275, 278–9, 284, 286,
287, 291, 297, 298, 301, 304, 307, 311
panic disorder 31–2, 38, 79
parenthood
    adapting to 6, 10–11, 230
    adjustments 18–25
    attitudes to mothers 14–15
    early months, managing 241–2
    expectations 5–8, 17, 26, 253–5, 261
    myths 253–5, 256
    Perfect Parent Syndrome 9–10
    period of adjustment 23
    practical ideas 242–6
    preparation 9–12
    reality 10–13, 17, 23, 24, 28
    resilience 13
    transition to 9–26
    websites 289–90
parenting skills 15–16
    personal experiences 15–16
    role models 16